Pelican Book A720
The World in 1984: Volume 1

The World in 1984

VOLUME I

The complete *New Scientist* series
Edited by Nigel Calder

PENGUIN BOOKS

Penguin Books Ltd, Harmondsworth,
Middlesex, England
Penguin Books Inc., 3300 Clipper Mill Road,
Baltimore 11, Md, U.S.A.
Penguin Books Pty Ltd, Ringwood,
Victoria, Australia
First published by *New Scientist* 1964
Published in Penguin Books 1965

Made and printed in Great Britain by
Cox and Wyman Ltd, London, Reading,
and Fakenham

Set in Monotype Plantin

Contents

Introduction

In 1964, about 100 men and women from many countries, distinguished in learning and practical affairs, contributed to *New Scientist* on the likely developments of the next twenty years. Their articles are here brought together in a convenient form in two volumes. This first volume is primarily scientific and technical; the second deals with broader subjects, such as government, domestic life, leisure, and development in different regions. Yet the contributions show a disregard for the conventional departments of thought: there is plenty of general interest in Volume 1 and plenty of science in Volume 2.

As far as I know, no journal has ever attempted to forecast the future in this way or on this scale, and a word of explanation should be given. There is growing awareness that rates of change are now so great that medium-range forecasts are a serious requirement if we are not to be caught out by change and if the scientific revolution is to be carried through wisely. But isolated forecasts by individuals tend to centre on a few ideas and overlook the fact that the world of the future, like the world of the present, is a complex system of many technical and human elements. A comprehensive approach is required if important factors are not to be missed. One way would be methodical studies by a group of scientists and others, collecting and analysing data on the technical and social trends, as a research project. That, however, is a method more appropriate to a research institution than to a journal. *New Scientist* chose to obtain contributions from authorities in the various fields, each of which would be intrinsically interesting, but to do it on a sufficient scale to take most of the foreseeable factors into account. There is some overlap between fields, and conflicts of opinion are manifest. Authors were asked to exercise their imaginations, but the basis was to be in known possibilities. A time-scale of twenty years was chosen because it demands more than the restatement of present trends, and yet we can suppose that things likely to be socially important in 1984 will already be in the laboratory or exist as ideas. This opinion is endorsed by Lord Todd: 'In most fields of technology . . . the time lag between a really fundamental discovery in science and its widespread application is rarely less than twenty years.' Even so, a certain amount of guesswork is unavoidable and unforeseeable discoveries could radically alter the picture.   NIGEL CALDER

Science and Human Goals

A BRITISH VIEW: WORKING WITH WHAT WE KNOW

by Professor Lord Todd, F.R.S.

One of the major difficulties in trying to make predictions about the next twenty years is that, if past history is any guide, such unforeseen events as major and prolonged wars or revolutions could throw them out completely. Over very long periods the effect of such aberrations may be of much less importance, but in the short term they can entirely alter the picture. I therefore start on the assumption – and I am optimist enough to believe it a reasonable one – that there will be no world war during the period we are considering.

What are human goals ? Basically man seeks freedom from hunger and want, adequate warmth and protection, and freedom from disease. Added to these he wants reasonable leisure and recreation and with these the freedom to seek an understanding of the workings of the universe in which he lives. These seem to me the main goals of humanity in 1964 as they were in 1864 or 1064; I have no reason to doubt that they will still be its goals in 1984 and they will still seem far off for many people. Progress towards them is, of course, being made continuously and more will be made in the next twenty years, but the situation is rather like that in highjumping at an athletics meeting – each time the bar is cleared it is raised another half-inch.

Before discussing likely advances, however, it is well to remember that in most fields of technology – and it is technological developments that are involved in most of the basic goals – the time-lag between a really fundamental discovery in science and its widespread application is rarely less than twenty years. This is not invariably so, of course – there are areas, in chemistry and biology, for example, where laboratory experiments and their practical use may be very close to one another. But, leaving these areas aside, it is probable that the seeds of any large-scale technological developments to be made in the next twenty years are already with us. In other words development of what we know today is likely to be of more practical consequence to mankind in 1984 than any spectacular new advance which may be made in pure science in the intervening period.

The problem of food production on a scale adequate to meet the needs of an ever-growing world population is clearly facing us now, and I would not expect it to be greatly mitigated by population control, which is unlikely to have a major effect in the course of twenty years, although the means whereby it could be achieved will certainly be available. There have been, during recent years, a variety of experimental studies on food production by cultivation of algae and yeasts or by extraction of leaf protein. Interesting as these methods are, the major developments are likely to be in more orthodox agriculture. I expect to see agricultural production doubled during the next twenty years, mainly by improvements in practice based on existing knowledge and by the controlled use of pesticides, many of them new products with a high degree of species specificity. Another factor is likely to be a slow decline in the use of land for producing materials (for example, rubber and fibres) which can be replaced by products of the chemical industry.

The extension of agricultural lands by rehabilitation of once fertile areas and the bringing into use of the world's vast areas of arid land, although it will occur on a modest scale, is likely to be a major preoccupation only towards the end of the century. Equally, although there will be a substantial increase in the productivity of fisheries through application of scientific knowledge and improvement in technique, I would not expect the conversion of fishing from a hunting to a farming operation to be far advanced before the 1990s.

Rising population and improved living standards associated with increasing industrialization are continually bringing fresh problems to both 'developed' and 'underdeveloped' countries. In the former, at least, the enormous problems of increasing urbanization – land use, building construction, transportation, and public health – will demand for their solution the help not only of the natural but also the so-called social sciences. I expect to see the emergence of the social sciences from their present rather rudimentary state into one in which, as coherent bodies of knowledge with established techniques of investigation, they will contribute greatly to human well-being. By 1984 a new approach to the urban community should be appearing which may presage entirely new methods of city development and intra-urban transportation. These will doubtless still be at the experimental stage, but substantial progress along these lines will have to be made if urban communities are not to strangle themselves by their own growth. Much of the scientific knowledge needed is already available.

The development of modern technologically based civilization brings with it increasing demands for power both for industry and for heating. Power production by conventional means has been enormously improved in recent years by technological development and this process will go further. Moreover, by 1984, the development and application of fast nuclear reactors will have reached a point at which nuclear energy will make a substantial contribution to world power needs. I do not expect that it will become the primary power source until we have been able to control the thermonuclear fusion reaction to obtain power from heavy hydrogen; this is likely to be solved in principle inside twenty years but its industrial application to give free access to thermonuclear power will only come later. Only then, of course, will the reservation of coal and oil to their proper use as chemical raw materials become practicable.

Freedom from disease is one of man's basic goals and in its pursuit substantial advances can be expected based in considerable measure on the new knowledge of the living cell now unfolding through the joint labours of the biologists, chemists, and physicists. The understanding which these studies are giving and are likely to give in the next ten years or so may well not merely enable us to understand the working of viruses and the nature of cancer, but will permit substantial advances in the treatment of the latter and of virus diseases by chemical agents. We should also, in the next twenty years, reach an understanding of at least some forms of mental illness and perhaps be able to eliminate them.

As all these developments occur, man is likely to have a considerable increase in leisure, arising mainly from a continuous extension of automation in industry, agriculture, and administration. Computer development, as yet in its infancy, will play a large part in this and it seems probable that the use of chemical molecules for information storage will find practical application in this field. When one recalls the amount of information which must be stored in the genetic material deoxyribonucleic acid (DNA), the possibilities of such an application would seem to be enormous. The widespread application of lasers and super-conductors will also have a marked effect on technological development.

Although I expect the present confusion in high-energy nuclear physics to be resolved by the development of a new theory of matter, this is not likely to have any marked effect on human progress for some time. Little of practical import, apart from satellite communications, is likely to result from space exploration, although during the next twenty years it will be further extended – probably in parallel with a running down of defence expenditures – and a landing on the moon may well be achieved.

Of much more significance will be results in the field of molecular biology, where a fuller understanding of the genetic code and its significance may, in the next twenty years, have indicated the way to the modification of biological control systems based on nucleic acids. We may stand in 1984 before developments in the control and modification of living systems that will be fraught with incalculable possibilities for mankind.

AN AMERICAN VIEW: THE SCIENTIST IN PUBLIC AFFAIRS

by Professor I. I. Rabi

'Here's to pure mathematics, may it never find an application.' This celebrated toast is attributed to the mathematician G. H. Hardy. Here 'application' meant nothing less than pure physics tainted at birth with the empirical. Presumably mathematics for Hardy was an end in itself, its values internal and largely aesthetic, set apart from other human goals and perceptions. Despite the war and its aftermath, this attitude continues in mathematics and has found some emulation in some parts of physics. This is not the first time in intellectual history that fashion has triumphed over function.

Despite this aloofness of mathematicians, their work is applied more and more in the pure sciences and applied sciences, and provides an unfailing source of kudos for mathematicians. Mathematics is not the only scientific activity that does good by indirection. Indeed, it can be said that all science does better than its practitioners know.

It is a characteristic of scientists in general that they have no flair for predicting the future. That is better done by the H. G. Wellses and Aldous Huxleys. The scientist may have 'future in his bones', as Sir Charles Snow puts it, but alas not at the tip of his tongue. Science may be the engine of social, economic, military, industrial, and intellectual change, but the scientist is not in the driver's seat. To continue the metaphor, until the Second World War he hardly raised his head above the bonnet.

The reasons are simple, even though inexcusable. The interval between discovery and application was long, the number of scientists small, and their support meagre. Science was therefore only peripherally in the field of vision of the treasury, of the foreign office, and even of the military. The scientists had enough to keep them busy and were in no mood to breach the ramparts of the establishment defended in depth by the warriors of the 'other culture'.

The basic conditions are now reversed, the tempo of application is rapid, the number of scientists is much greater and rapidly growing. Support runs from ample to lavish and some scientists have at least a finger on the wheel. These changes cannot be other than good. There is hardly a problem of government that does not have an important scientific aspect.

Agriculture, public health, and medicine are more and more matters of governmental concern. In defence, although the enduring military principles may remain, their implementation is increasingly a matter of advanced, rapidly changing, and highly expensive technology and science. Science permeates the field, from nuclear warheads to the training and feeding of personnel. In foreign affairs the scientific vigour of a nation is an important element of its prestige because it is in some measure an element of its future strength and importance, either in friendly alliance or in competition. Over and above these considerations, there is the attitude of objectivity and clarity which distinguishes the scientific approach to any problem – even those, and perhaps especially those, in which chance and the human factor play a large role.

There is probably no country where the educational system does not require a fundamental reform to take care of present and future needs and circumstances. Perhaps with the exception of Russia, the curriculum badly needs expansion in the scientific fields and not only for scientists but for every walk of life. With a rapidly changing science, only the most highly qualified scientists can help the educator and government give direction to these changes. It is amazing how long outdated science can survive in school curricula.

The scientist cannot be fully effective when he is only an outside consultant because it takes a scientist to recognize the elements of the situation where science can contribute. President Eisenhower appointed his first Special Assistant for Science and Technology in 1957. It did not take very long for him to realize the enormous support he was able to receive from a scientist continuously available in intimate contact with his problems and capable of drawing on the scientific community for further help. This office is now an established institution in the United States and used more and more each year.

The scientist brings to government not only knowledge and a certain discipline but also a quality of freshness, a faith in progress in every direction, and, even more, a feeling for the possibilities of development or evolution in a current situation. The universality of science also brings with it a certain sense of rightness and equity, sometimes naïve but rarely on the wrong track. We can look for a further development of the relations between science and government and, with greater difficulty, science and industry. The experience of the war and post-war years has given many scientists experience in affairs which should make the influence felt more and more. We may expect in the future to see more scientists on the boards of industrial concerns as well as on advisory committees of government.

There is one vital field where scientists have made hardly any contribution and that is to politics – politics in its practical sense of standing for office. Somehow the scientific education diminishes the ambition for power and worldly influence. Perhaps it is only the tribal feeling instilled by an élite which considers political activity a desertion of the true cause. None the less, the influence of science is sorely missed in the parliaments of the world.

If science were taught more humanistically in the schools and in the universities, it could become a foundation for any career, not only teaching or research. The entry of these new men with the momentum of the scientific culture combined with the older, more classical elements could give a hybrid vigour to our civilization.

Without such a combination we can hardly expect to 'face down' the perils of an age of nuclear weapons and of automation, of affluent societies in the midst of an almost global morass of ignorance, disease, and poverty. The desire and will to make a more equitable world exist, and not only in the youth. The success of the Peace Corps in the United States would have been impossible without this spirit. If the time is ripe, as it seems to be, the bold and understanding leadership must surely come.

Science itself is badly in need of integration and unification. The tendency is more and more the other way. To take physics as an example, theoretical physicists are separate from experimenters. Each of these groups in turn breaks up in separate specialities, such as particle physics, nuclear physics, solid-state physics, plasma physics, field theory and dispersion theory, statistical mechanics, etc. Only the graduate student, poor beast of burden that he is, can be expected to know a little of each. As the number of physicists increases, each speciality becomes more self-sustaining and self-contained. Such Balkanization carries physics and, indeed, every science, farther and farther away from natural philosophy, which, intellectually, is the meaning and goal of science.

We must regard the growth of knowledge as a good thing, and specialization there must be if science is to advance and fulfil human needs and the desire for knowledge. None the less, we must have some people who prefer to survey the whole. Here the universities can make their special contribution. If each of them would function as a community rather than as an assembly of scholars, these separate disciplines would discover new connexions and the scholar would occasionally lift his head and survey the horizon.

THE LESS-DEVELOPED WORLD: HOW CAN WE BE OPTIMISTS?

by Professor Abdus Salam, F.R.S.

'Between the frontiers of the three super-states Eurasia, Oceania, and Eastasia, and not permanently in possession of any of them, there lies a rough quadrilateral with its corners at Tangier, Brazzaville, Darwin, and Hongkong. These territories contain a bottomless reserve of cheap labour. Whichever power controls equatorial Africa, or the Middle East or Southern India or the Indonesian Archipelago, disposes also of the bodies of hundreds of millions of ill-paid and hard-working coolies, expended by their conquerors like so much coal or oil in the race to turn out more armaments, to capture more territory, to control more labour, to turn out more armaments, to capture more territory, to control...' Thus George Orwell – in his only reference to the less-developed world.

I wish I could disagree with him. Orwell may have erred in not anticipating the withering of direct colonial controls within the 'quadrilateral' he speaks about; he may not quite have gauged the vehemence of urges to political self-assertion. Nor, dare I hope, was he right in the sombre picture of conscious and heartless exploitation he has painted. But he did not err in predicting persisting poverty and hunger and overcrowding in 1984 among the less privileged nations.

I would like to live to regret my words but twenty years from now, I am positive, the less-developed world will be as hungry, as relatively undeveloped, and as desperately poor, as today. And this, despite the fact that we know the world has enough resources – technical, scientific, and material – to eliminate poverty, disease, and early death, for the whole human race.

The visible portents of 1984 are there for all to see. Notwithstanding every physical and ideological exhortation, the agricultural production of all but the richest countries is static. It would seem that the industry of food production is as investment-intensive as any other. We are only just beginning to speak, in not too muted tones, of high birth-rates. There are none among the rich nations willing enough to sponsor a fair price structure for the commodity market – the one major resource the poorer countries possess for financing their meagre development plans. There are likely to be higher and still higher tariff walls against their cheap manufactures. And every year the battle to keep the trickle of foreign aid programmes flowing becomes fiercer and fiercer. The United Nations Development Decade from all indications is likely to end with a whimper.

But this is not what makes me so utterly pessimistic. Never in the history of mankind has a change happened all at once. The one great change of the first half of this century – the passing of the Colonial Age – was the culmination of fifty years of crusading. In most places it all started with a few men, whose passionate fury first overwhelmed their own peoples and then succeeded in rousing the liberal conscience of their captors, bringing home to them also the utter economic futility of holding down an unwilling people. This is the normal process of change. What makes me worried is that no such thing has yet happened in the under-developed world so far as the harder crusade against poverty is concerned. And in the few places where realization has come, it has not been purposeful enough yet to bring down the internal social and the organizational barriers, nor to be able to defy external pressures. In the next twenty years I trust this crusade will come to be preached with the fury it deserves within the poorer countries. I can only hope it remains inward-turning – that it does not become a destructive wave of antagonism against those fortunate few among the nations of the world who somehow inherited most of this earth's resources and do not quite need them all.

But this will take time. For 1984 itself, I am resigned to Orwell's grim picture, with want and misery unchecked – unless, of course, there rises earlier somewhere a new Messiah, the one who can preach that in this age when technological miracles are indeed possible the raising of living standards everywhere to a decent human level is first and foremost a moral problem, and a collective world responsibility.

Fundamental Science

TOWARDS A BETTER UNDERSTANDING OF NATURAL FORCES

by Sir John Cockcroft, O.M., F.R.S.

Master of Churchill College, Cambridge

Speculations about the work in fundamental science twenty years ahead must necessarily be very uncertain, for who was prophetic enough to foresee nuclear fission or the coming of radio astronomy in 1932? Nevertheless, we have today some indication of the course of development in many branches of fundamental science, if only because we have many unanswered questions and good prospects of progress towards obtaining the answers.

One of the most fundamental problems is to obtain a better understanding of the relations between the four main forces of the universe – the gravitational, electromagnetic, and strong and weak nuclear interactions. It will probably be a long time before we can bring the gravitational forces within a general theory, since there is at present no progress in this direction. On the other hand, considerable progress is being made in the study of the phenomena associated with strong and weak nuclear interactions. We are accumulating more and more information on the masses and spins of the arrays of mesons and the excited states of nucleons, and getting a better understanding of their symmetries and patterns which must be related to the strong nuclear forces. This may well enable us to give a dynamical explanation of why the strongly interacting particles have their particular mass values.

The experiments at Brookhaven and CERN with beams of energetic neutrinos from the decay of pions have already led to the accumulation of data on the very weak interaction of neutrinos with nuclei, leading to the production of pions and a confirmation that two kinds of neutrinos exist. The experiments are on the point of revealing more information about the mechanism of these interactions and their variation with neutrino energy. This kind of experiment will be helped if a 'next generation' of nuclear accelerators is built to produce protons in the 300-GeV energy region. Accelerators of this energy will be unlikely to come into commission before 1972.

Another unanswered question concerns the role of the muon, which also interacts weakly with atomic nuclei and appears to behave in many ways like a heavy electron.

The attainment of strong beams of protons at 300-GeV energy will not only extend our present range of experiments but may, if our previous experience is a guide, uncover new kinds of nuclear phenomena at present not envisaged.

The theories of cosmology and the birth and development of stars are likely to be put on firmer foundations by the continued cooperation of optical and radio astronomers. Their work will be helped by the more powerful and discriminating radio telescopes which have recently come into operation or are being built or designed today. New southern-hemisphere optical telescopes of the 150-inch class may come into commission to help to interpret the observations of southern-hemisphere radio telescopes. We had a good example of such collaboration by Mount Palomar discovering that a new radio source was so intense that, according to Professor Fred Hoyle, it could have resulted from the gravitational collapse of a whole galaxy. Instrumentation is likely to be improved also by the coming into use of 36-inch telescopes mounted in satellites, with stabilization accurate to within a second of arc. They will provide astronomers with photographs undisturbed by atmospheric turbulence and with records of ultra-violet and soft X-ray emissions. The accumulation of data on the distribution of distant stars may enable us to make more plausible theories on the origin of the universe.

The developing interest in the origins of life on our planet, starting with the fossil evidence from rocks three billion years old and theories of the mechanism of synthesis of complex molecules in the primeval ocean, may receive further experimental material from instruments landed on Mars to determine what kind, if any, of complex molecules have been fabricated in that environment.

There are certain to be continuing developments in classical physics, where the basic laws are well known – in fluid mechanics, magneto-hydrodynamics, superconductivity, geophysics, solid-state physics.

In the field of magneto-hydrodynamics, we will no doubt continue to improve our theoretical understanding of the behaviour of very hot plasmas and of their numerous varieties of instabilities. We are making advances in our ability to suppress some of the instabilities by shaping of magnetic fields, but we have still a factor of many orders of magnitude to gain before a practical nuclear fusion reactor is in sight. It is impossible, at present, to predict whether this will be achieved by 1984. Probably before then other applications of magneto-hydrodynamics, such as large-scale direct conversion of heat to electricity requiring only modest plasma temperatures of a few thousand degrees, will have been achieved in practice.

The solid-state physicist will no doubt make further advances in the borderline between pure and applied science. Our understanding of the behaviour of metals and alloys will increase with our increasing basic knowledge, helped by tools such as the transmission electron microscope, the field ion microscope, and neutron scattering from crystals. Lasers may, by 1984, have led to important new developments in communications, because of the great potential information-carrying capacity of modulated light beams. They are likely to improve frequency standards and so provide an important tool for geodesy and metrology. There will undoubtedly be great progress in micro-miniaturization in electronics and in the development of superconducting information storage systems, leading, we hope, to smaller, more reliable, cheaper, and faster computers, thus helping basic science and mathematics still more.

The chemists will, no doubt, make equally notable advances. Already DNA has been bio-synthesized from its four basic building blocks put together with the enzyme polymerase and some natural DNA to act as a template, and genetically deficient bacteria have substituted good DNA for bad. Perhaps there will be some progress towards curing inborn disorder in man. More immediate, perhaps, are the possibilities, suggested by the Royal Society report on the biological sciences, of manipulating the genetic structure of harmful insects, and the ideas of other biologists about fabrication of viruses or modification of their structures.

Considerable progress seems likely in the control of fertility by bio-chemical means, and by 1984 we may have made some progress in applying this to the control of the population explosion in many countries.

DYNAMICAL SYSTEMS IN PHYSICS AND BIOLOGY

by Professor Norbert Wiener

Department of Mathematics, Massachusetts Institute of Technology

In writing about this theme, I shall have to make many guesses, which, if they are valid, will in many cases be realized well before 1984. Thus the date can have no great significance, and what I am really writing about are suggestions as to the way that fundamental science is going now. The most dangerous of all predictions would be a too-narrow projection into the future of the details of science at the present time. The things of which I am going to speak are already in the nascent state, and have come to my attention by the convergence of work being done in many fields all over the world.

There is a general feeling that the multiplicity of fundamental particles in physics is intolerable and is bound to be replaced in the near future by a much more unified physics in which both quantum theory and relativity are to be recast and in which the origin and disintegration of fundamental particles will be of the nature of quantum jumps. There is also a strong indication that quantum physics is only the gross manifestation of phenomena on a much smaller scale of space and time which will be closely assimilated to a classical deterministic theory in which any indeterminism arises purely from our inability to work in any other mode than statistically on these very small-scale phenomena. In this deterministic theory many of the fundamental difficulties of relativity will disappear because the small-scale system which I have mentioned will involve continuous variables and will avoid action at a distance. In connexion with this, I should like to mention the work of Professor J. L. Synge of Dublin and of the group centring around De Broglie, Vigier, and Bohm (see *Physical Review*, Vol. 129, p. 438). Dr G. Della Riccia of the Institute of Theoretical Physics at the University of Naples and I are also working in this direction, in which a fundamental idea is that in quantum physics and mechanics the study of the organization of systems will play a large part.

The main problems of biology also have to do with systems and their organization in time and space. Here, self-organization is bound to play a great role. Therefore, what I predict for the life sciences is not merely their progressive assimilation to physics, but a progressive assimilation of physics to the life sciences.

There are many points which are suggestive for the future of the life sciences and in which I hesitate to make too sharp a distinction between fundamental science and techniques. One of these is the ever-growing importance given to the nucleic acids and their reproduction. It is becoming abundantly clear that the nucleic acid complexes not only play a fundamental role in genetic memory, but that they probably play an analogous role in nervous memory. Physiologically, it has also become clear that genetics, the study of viruses, and the study of cancer are really varying branches of nucleic acid chemistry and of the study of structures dependent on such chemistry. I also anticipate that this same nucleic acid chemistry will carry over to the study of enzymes, immunity reactions, and the like. Dr Edmond Dewan of Brandeis University and the Massachusetts General Hospital has pointed out to me that the disorganization of the nervous system which is found in schizophrenia and other mental diseases may not be entirely independent of the type of genetic disorganization which occurs in cancer.

In connexion with nervous memory and the role of the nucleic acid complexes, I think it is quite possible that the memory properties of such complexes may be used in machines which need an artificial memory and that, just as we have the peak of the technique of solid-state physics, so the next generation will see the use of nucleic acids as valuable engineering materials.

In any case, I am reasonably confident that the studies of dynamical systems which I have mentioned are relevant to problems of biological organization. The apparent role of the nucleic acids in the nervous system is going to lead to a new neurology in which long-time storage of information will probably be largely dependent on the nucleic acids or associated compounds. The nervous system will have to be regarded more and more, not as a static network, but as a network which is alive and changing its internal configurations with experience. Here we shall have to step well away from the preoccupation of biologists with the cell. The fact that nerve cells do not multiply after birth does not prevent the continual growth and reorganization of the connexions in the nervous system between cells. For short-time phenomena we shall still have to emphasize the neural network, as far as its connexions at any given time go, as the basis of sensation, motor action, and reflexes. Still, we cannot treat it as if it were a computing machine network fixed for all time, and we shall have to consider the interplay of what Professor Francis Schmitt of M.I.T. calls 'dry' neurophysiology, dealing with the established nervous network, and 'wet' physiology, which is going to centre more and more about the nucleic acids.

With an ever-increasing understanding of memory and its mechanisms, psychology, which has been largely a phenomenological science, is going to become more and more tied up with neurophysiology. Many other considerations which have up to the present been situated in a somewhat shameful background, such as the study of direct communication at a distance between nervous systems, possibly by some sort of radiative phenomenon, are going to be subjected to a real trend in scientific examination which will not be corrupted by the unscientific assumption that we are dealing with phenomena with no physical correlates. I am looking forward with some confidence either to seeing physical correlates discovered for these phenomena if they do exist, which I regard as quite possible, or to their finally being pushed out of consideration.

I am looking forward to the growth in studies of dynamical systems, not merely for the sake of fundamental physiology, as I have already indicated, but also for techniques of healing or ameliorating human deficiencies. The taking of signals in and out of the body higher up in the nervous system than in our sense organs and muscles, by the amplification and manipulation of nerve impulses, is well under way in work conducted jointly by members of the Massachusetts General Hospital and M.I.T. This bids fair for the development of artificial limbs which can be used in a thoroughly voluntary way by the employment of existing nerve channels and with a minimum distortion of the personality. On the other hand, in internal medicine, an analogous procedure is already beginning to be developed. For example, Dr John Lyman and his group at Los Angeles are studying the handling of diabetes by a continuous sensing of the blood-sugar level to enable insulin to be released, not according to the clock, but according to the instantaneous physiological need. This type of 'artificial homeostasis' represents an extension of the ideas used in the artificial pacemaker for the heart. I am looking forward to such developments not merely as a direct technique for the treatment of people under a physiological disability, but as a powerful experimental tool in the development of what I expect to be a new medicine.

A CRISIS IN EVOLUTION

by Professor Joshua Lederberg

Director, Kennedy Laboratories for Molecular Medicine, Stanford University School of Medicine, California

Through its association with medicine, agriculture, and conservation, biological science has been concerned in the most constructive of material advances in the human condition. The sudden successes of biology, brought about through systematic confluence with the physical sciences, now demand an understanding of the nature and destiny of man that must be the principal intellectual task of the brave new world.

This assessment takes for granted the filling in of immense detail on the framework of molecular biology. The magnitude of present efforts, and their constant acceleration, make this the only sensible direction. The application of these findings, especially to man himself, looms as a larger problem than quite unpredictable departures in basic theoretical outlook.

In fact, the main theoretical foundations of biology are simply the conception of life as a chemical mechanism, a manifestation of molecular architecture, and the evolutionary elaboration of this mechanism through random variation and natural selection. These skeletal ideas were contributions of a previous generation – Pasteur and Bernard, Darwin, Mendel and Morgan, the patriarchal German organic chemists – and recent biology has contributed nothing so iconoclastic in basic theory to match the finesse of its experimental demonstrations and technical power. If new theoretical principles are to emerge – and who can tell? – they may well arise either from the mathematical study of complex organization needed to understand brains, computer programmes, and societies, or from the generalization of terrestrial life, by the observation of planetary life or intelligent communication with other living systems or by the contrived synthesis of new organisms in the laboratory. Until then, the main distinction between physics and biology may continue to be the relative weight of universal axiom and parochial detail.

Prophecy is a just target for irony, but planning for the next twenty to fifty years is a major responsibility of our political and intellectual leaders. The exigent time scale of the evolutionary crisis still has not captured their attention.

For aeons, the evolution of this planet proceeded by random chemistry. After the spark of life was struck, for one, perhaps two billion years, life evolved with ever-increasing complexity, but with few basic changes in quality. Some hundred thousand years ago, a species emerged able to communicate and thus to accumulate tradition, and generate the explosion of history. In that brief interval, our evolution has been principally cultural. Man, the historical animal, practises his civilization with the same biological instruments as the Neanderthal. Just in the instant era, our culture is achieving knowledge and control of its biological instruments that are capable of purposefully altering them. At the same time we are evolving other instruments (informational machinery, or computers) which share with man the generation of culture. Should our planning, even for the next twenty years, wait till after the event to react to revolutionary changes in human nature?

What is new in these remarks? The success of quantitative methods in plant and animal breeding soon aroused a series of eugenic schemes to counteract the irrelevance – at best – of social criteria and reproductive flux. To varying degrees, these schemes have evoked worse social evils. Furthermore, our limited knowledge of human genetics left one certainty: that any acceptable level of selection could insignificantly alter the gene pool of any large community on the time scale of cultural evolution. The net effect has been the relegation of many biologists' thinking on human evolution to an area of dubious efficacy, and of many others' to the view that there was a comfortably long time during which not to worry about it; meanwhile we could all be more happily preoccupied with the Bomb, with fall-out, with the population explosion, and with pesticides. And, rightly, our colleagues have not been deeply impressed with forebodings that molecular biology would soon give us the capability of directly altering or producing the human gene string.

However, the debate should not be allowed to peter out. It should be our responsibility to assess the future with at least the more plausible predictions of biological capability. This is a tricky and strenuous enterprise, and deserves both more imagination and more critical judgement than have been spent on it so far. In doing so, we should not let customary scientific conservatism blind us from noting how new advances themselves accelerate the pace of technical advance, and how far the orientation of all the earth's subcultures, especially in mutual conflict, towards technical power, accelerates the practical application of scientific findings. The last point should also answer any wistful hopes that science itself might be muted.

The riskiest elements of this essay are specific predictions of the technical problems that are about to be solved to the augmentation of man's powers and his dilemmas. May I enter some suggestions only to illustrate the genus of possibilities; they centre on the modification of development, influencing the character of single organisms, in contrast to the populational impact of eugenic measures. Hence we may call them 'euphenic'. The reader should use his own judgement as to the probable implementation of euphenics in the actual world, and its significance for individual man and his culture.

(1) The successful transplantation of vital organs: heart, liver, limbs. The technical barriers will be overcome long before we can reach a moral concensus on the organization of the market for allocation of precious parts.

(2) Artificial prosthetic organs. Unfortunately not yet being developed with the necessary vigour to overtake the preceding.

(3) In consequence of these, and probably other advances in, say, protein biochemistry, a sudden increase in the expectation,

or prolongability, of life. With a wider range of technical resources will come a corresponding expansion of the scale of the useful cost of maintaining a given personality. Whatever our humanitarian predilections, discrepancies in the availability of these resources must widen.

(4) More optimistically, the modification of the developing human brain through treatment of the foetus or infant. At least some modifications (like those used primitively now in the control of metabolic disease) can be expected to be constructively applied to 'normal' children, and might well exceed the present bounds of genetic and developmental variation.

(5) 'Clonal' reproduction, through nuclear transplantation. The prototype for this suggestion is the transplantation of a nucleus from an adult tissue cell back into an amphibian egg from which the natural nucleus has been removed, with (sometimes) normal development of this egg. It should be recalled that vegetative reproduction, occasionally concealed under outward trappings of sexuality, is an important feature of the plant world, and a few primitive animals. The experiment has yet to be attempted in a mammal. Apart from its place in the narcissistic perpetuation of a given genotype, the technique would have an enormous impact on predetermination of sex; on the avoidance of hereditary abnormalities, as well as positive eugenics; on cultural acceleration through education within a clone; and on more far-reaching experiments on the reconstitution of the human genotype.

Perhaps enough has been said, though this is far from the end of the list. I will be accused of demonic advocacy (and have been) for discussing such matters and not pretending that they are indefinitely far off. But they are inseparable from the advance of medicine, especially as we turn our attention to such urgent challenges as mental retardation, the degeneration of ageing, and mental illness.

The scientific community has little special qualification to impose institutional remedies or moral criteria for the problems of human opportunity. It has the responsibility to teach these problems especially in the university, and to look for imbalances in our technical capability. For example, the grievous social stresses that organ transplantation will engender would be mitigated by the parallel development of artificial organs, or the availability of animal sources. If clonal reproduction becomes possible, or more simply, if present suggestions on the hormonal induction of twinnings are verified, we will wish we knew much more about the biology and psychology of twins.

Meanwhile, a deeper understanding of our present knowledge of human biology must be part of the insight of literary, political, social, economic, and moral teaching; it is far too important to be left only to the biologists. In this spirit I can think of no better dedication than to the memory of the prophetic vision and artistic clarity of Aldous Huxley.

Astronomy and Space Exploration

A NEW PHYSICS OUT OF ASTRONOMY?

by Professor Fred Hoyle, F.R.S.

University of Cambridge

Much of what happens in astronomy between now and 1984 will depend on the possible mergers between astronomy in the classical sense and newer disciplines. By 1984 the present-day distinction between 'optical' astronomy and 'radio' astronomy will probably have disappeared. Close cooperation is already necessary in many of the most interesting problems. Moreover, the optical astronomer is becoming increasingly electronics-minded, so that the methods used by radio astronomers no longer appear as mysterious as they once did.

The identification of radio sources is an outstandingly important example of this cooperation. By pointing a large optical telescope at the positions measured by radio astronomers very remarkable results are being obtained, almost month by month. So far, however, only those 100 or so sources of greatest apparent radio intensity have been examined in this way, and the majority of them have been identified with optically visible objects. During the next decade it is certain that this work will be extended to fainter sources. Within five to ten years a sufficient number of identifications will probably have been made for the luminosity function of radio sources to be determined – i.e. the distribution of sources with respect to intrinsic intensity. Only then can we know the distance of a typical source of specified apparent intensity. This knowledge is necessary for many purposes, in particular to interpret the source counts obtained by Professor Martin Ryle and his colleagues. Do these counts really refer to an early stage in the history of the universe, or are we looking at a shell of sources some two or three billion light years away? Either way, the issue is one of great interest to cosmology, but the interest lies in very different directions in the two cases.

The relation of astronomy and space research is fraught with much greater uncertainty, although in one direction we already have an example of a similar encouraging cooperation – in the developing subject of X-rays and gamma-rays from outside the solar system. Such observations, made from spacecraft above the atmosphere, place limits on cosmic-ray fluxes inside and outside galaxies, and this in turn has relevance for the study of the origin of cosmic rays, whether in supernovae (exploding stars) or in still more violent events. It may also turn out that this work has relevance to the formation of galaxies themselves.

But the astronomer cannot avoid some misgivings about the relation of his subject to space research – more particularly in the United States and the Soviet Union than smaller countries, perhaps. To be sure, an orbiting observatory would be an enormous asset to astronomy, but the prospects for such an observatory seem to have been stated in over-optimistic terms, to say the least. The situation between astronomy and space research has more than a superficial resemblance to a commercial competition between two companies, one small with a gross turnover of a few millions a year, the other a vast corporation with annual turnover well in excess of £1,000 m. The inevitable evolution would be for the large company to take over the small one.

'Why not ?' it may be asked. Because of radically different basic motivations. Astronomy always has been, and still is, studied out of an inherent curiosity about the nature and structure of the universe. Big Science is not supported for this reason. Accelerator physics is supported by governments because of memories of the bomb and because of the promise of nuclear energy. Space activities owe their origin to the cold war, and to the economic necessity in the United States of supporting a declining aircraft industry. Space spells prosperity, as well as providing a new kind of gladiatorial show. The astronomer does well to ask himself whether he wishes his subject to be submerged in a frenzy of ballyhoo – for example, the description of the flight of *Mariner 2* as 'man's greatest astronomical adventure since Galileo'.

Turning now to the relation of astronomy to physics, in recent decades physicists have tended to view astronomy in a rather unfavourable light. Astronomers are thought of as queer people, sleeping all day, living on mountains, given to wild assertion, and never concerned with anything fundamental. In so far as it derives from a respectable source, this view is based I think on the following argument. Physics is concerned with particles and with their interactions. All interactions are local, and can be discovered by local experiment. Hence all physical laws can be discovered without stirring outside the laboratory. So astronomy can have nothing fundamental to offer.

For myself, I do not concede this argument. What can one hope to discover by local experiment except local couplings between particles? Long-range couplings, such as those envisaged in which local forces might be determined by the nature of the universe as a whole, would stay untested, since we cannot shift the whole universe around in our experiments. If both local and long-range couplings exist, and the latter are undiscovered, fundamental physics will remain a hotch-potch of elegance and ugliness, as full of prescriptions as a chemist's shop, exactly as it looks today. And physics is indeed appallingly ugly, with the strange numerical values it finds for its various coupling constants and other quantities.

My suspicion is that important long-range couplings do exist and that many of the quantities we normally think of as constants are subject to a slow variation with time. By a slow variation, I mean slow compared with the rate at which existing galaxies are moving apart. On this basis, the precise values of some of the key constants of physics would have no absolute significance – they would simply belong to the epoch at which we happen to live.

Finally, then, my long-range prediction is that astronomy will some day introduce a major revolution into physics. It may have happened by 1984.

SCIENTIFIC PURPOSES IN SPACE

by Professor Sir Harrie Massey, F.R.S.

University College, London

The first satellite was launched less than seven years ago. Progress in the scientific investigation of the earth's environment in space has been very rapid and is continuing at an increasing rate. In view of this, twenty years ahead is a very long time and it is inevitable that, in making any forecasts so far ahead, the most novel and remarkable developments which will actually occur will not be imagined. However, there are many directions in which space research is now proceeding which can be clearly discerned.

The earth's atmosphere and its surroundings in interplanetary space are very strongly influenced by the sun. Solar ultra-violet and X-radiations produce the ionosphere which has played such a vital part in radio communications. These radiations also determine very many other aspects of atmospheric composition and behaviour such as the production of ozone and atomic oxygen. Streams of charged particles from the sun affect the ionosphere at high altitudes, produce magnetic storms and auroral displays and modify the intensity of cosmic rays received at the earth. These solar influences, particularly those transmitted through X-rays and charged particle streams, are not constant but vary in a semi-regular fashion in an 11-year cycle. In twenty years time we will have passed nearly through two further cycles, a matter of some significance.

None of the solar radiations referred to can be observed on the ground; they must be studied with instruments aboard space vehicles. Before twenty years have passed, solar patrols should have been established in the form of satellites carrying instruments which will monitor continually the intensity of solar ultra-violet and X-rays in different wavelength regions. This information will be transmitted regularly to the earth on command from a wide international network of stations. The importance of such systematic information, both for our understanding of the behaviour of the sun and of the way in which it influences our atmosphere, will be immense. Other satellites will contain appropriate instruments for monitoring various atmospheric properties. In short, the study of the electromagnetic radiation from the sun and its atmospheric effects will have reached the synoptic stage. With the opportunity for observation over two complete solar cycles, the main features will have become clear and the 'fine structure' will be under investigation.

The situation will be less advanced in the study of solar particle streams and their atmospheric effects. This is because it is much more complex due to the influence of the earth's magnetic field which causes the charged particles to pursue very complicated paths during their passage from the sun. Local magnetism in the emitting regions of the sun also complicates the picture. While in twenty years' time we should have a much clearer understanding of the various possibilities it is too much to expect that even the main features of such phenomena as magnetic storms, auroral displays, and the great particle radiation (Van Allen) belts will be thoroughly interpreted. Nevertheless patrol satellites following highly eccentric orbits will be in operation to monitor solar particle radiation, while it is likely that lunar observatories for this purpose will be established, on the moon, in the form of lunar satellites, or both.

Looking inwards will be a network of meteorological satellites fully and firmly integrated into a world system. In twenty years' time regular information about weather conditions from these vehicles will be the most important source of material for weather forecasters. Such material will be available on a worldwide basis without the huge gaps left in ground observations due to large areas of ocean or desert. The reliability of forecasts will be greatly improved and extended to longer periods. In this direction the value of international collaboration is so obvious that it will have developed to the good of all.

Paradoxically, the region of the atmosphere at altitudes above that attainable by balloons (20 km) out to about 150–200 km will be less thoroughly studied. This is because satellites cannot circulate for long within these altitudes. At first it will continue to be necessary to use vertical sounding rockets, which are only up for a few minutes, but at a later stage means for correcting effects of atmospheric friction on satellites will probably be developed so that they can remain in orbit for long periods at comparatively low altitudes.

By 1984 radio astronomers may well find that interference from many sources has made it very difficult to continue their observations effectively from the ground. In any case they will have developed an extensive programme for observations from satellites of the radio noise from our Galaxy and beyond, which is of too low a frequency to penetrate the earth's ionosphere. This will involve the use of elaborate and extensive aerials deployed from more than one space vehicle. The same techniques will permit of observations at other frequencies which could then be made free of terrestrial interference.

The mention of interference raises the question as to whether large-scale modifications of the earth's environment may not have been brought about which will have introduced serious extra-terrestrial sources of interference, not only for radio astronomy but for other scientific and general pursuits. During the twenty years the problem in this direction will have reached such proportions that a great deal of international discussion will be concerned with the setting up of a suitable system of controls to minimize dangers arising in this way. Although twenty years is a short time in which to expect any effective agreements, it is likely that the increase in cooperation between space scientists and technologists in different countries will be such that serious consequences of environmental modifications will be avoided.

Short-wave astronomy will be a well-established new subject involving the observation from space vehicles of ultra-violet and X-rays from the stars and other celestial objects. Orbiting observatories for this purpose will be as regular a feature as those for solar radiation patrols and atmospheric studies. They will provide elaborate on-board facilities so that the data transmitted to the ground will be already in a convenient form for study. The new discoveries which will be made cannot be predicted, but they will certainly be of great interest.

Probably the most exciting of all the scientific studies during the period will be those concerning life outside the earth. Instruments which can detect living organisms will have landed on the moon and particularly on Mars. Any positive indication from these instruments will be of profound importance and could lead to a thorough revaluation of the significance and nature of life.

The scientific study of the moon and the inner planets will have got under way and will have undoubtedly yielded many surprises which will have modified our views about the origin of the solar system.

A further direction in which the techniques of space research will be applied is the study of the nature of gravitation. This is technically more difficult than many other scientific applications. However, development in precision atomic clocks will have proceeded so far that a beginning will have been made in comparing the time recorded in such clocks aboard satellites with that recorded by exactly similar clocks on the ground. Measurements of this kind form the basis for checking theories of gravitation.

The facility with which scientific experiments can be carried out in space will have been greatly expanded through developments in high-speed computation and analysis, micro-miniaturization and electronics generally, and in communication through the use of maser and laser devices. In fact, the space vehicles will have come into use as laboratories for automatic research under high-vacuum conditions.

Finally, the contribution made by the expansion of space research to international understanding will be considerable, as by 1984 international collaboration between scientists and technologists will have become, of necessity, very close-knit.

TELECOMMUNICATIONS IN SPACE EXPLORATION

by Gerald C. Gross

Secretary-General, International Telecommunication Union

Telecommunications are the essential guide-lines to outer space. 90 per cent of the failures that have so far occurred in space equipment have been electronic failures. Telecommunications are totally dependent on electronics. Thus, there is no aspect of space techniques where improvement is more necessary than electronics and no kind of space activity for which this improvement is more vital than space exploration.

By 1984, the exploration of outer space will have become a regularly organized enterprise. Deep space probes will range far out towards the limits of the solar system, some returning after months or years and others simply vanishing into the silence when their work is done. There will be closely coordinated programmes for exploring the nearer regions of the solar system more intensively, with a number of specialized investigations for particular purposes.

One of the most striking differences between space exploration now and then is that, in all probability, most of the bases which control the space vehicles will be found, not on earth, but operating automatically on the surface of the moon. This will mean a communications network of incredible complexity, linking far-distant space probes to their bases, providing continuous control over the nearer space vehicles and channelling a vast stream of intelligence between the earth and the moon.

Moon Base

In all likelihood, the development of the moon as Space Research Base No. 1 will already be well advanced by the end of the 1970s. Why is the moon likely to be chosen for this purpose ? In the first place, it has all the advantages of being a natural launching and control platform beyond the influence of the earth's atmosphere. It is far bigger than any conceivable artificial satellite and the fact that it always turns the same face earthwards means that communications with the earth over super high radio frequencies (SHF) will be greatly simplified. Since the moon lacks an atmosphere, it should be free from such radio phenomena as fading and tropospheric and ionospheric scatter and from frequency selective effects due to atmospheric gaseous molecules and dust particles. The lack of an atmosphere on the moon also means the absence of winds, and this fact, taken together with the effect of low gravity, will make it possible to use quite remarkable antenna structures (aerials) impossible on earth.

The Moon Base will function as a repeater and encoder, using, for communications out into space, frequencies up to hundreds of gigacycles (10^{11} c/s). Lasers, due to the extreme purity of frequency of their signals and to the power they will handle, should greatly increase the range of space communications.

Space Communications

The moon, then, will be the base for space exploration – the platform which will provide space vehicles with their communications, ranging from great wide-band systems for nearer craft engaged in measurements and detailed observations, to the delicately-controlled transmissions directed to craft venturing towards the farther limits of the solar system.

Maintaining contact with distant space probes will be an immense undertaking, and already two basic problems can be foreseen. The first of these concerns the maximum distance at which a signal is detectable. This depends on the effective radiated power of the transmission and on the degree of sophistication of the reception arrangements, but nevertheless the distance in free space that can be effectively spanned will always be a finite one. For example, if a transmission loss of 200 decibels can be tolerated in a system at 12,000 megacycles, the system can be used across a distance of about 16,000 kilometres in free space. If distances of one million kilometres are to be attained, a system even more tolerant of loss – to the extent of over 230 decibels – would be required. Equipment capable of providing such performance as this is already known, so that, with perfected energy converters for spacecraft (the spacecraft-to-base direction is normally the weaker because of power considerations in space vehicles), we can expect that, by 1984, distances of many million kilometres will be within the scope of our radio equipment.

Another limiting factor is the level of incoming radio noise from the Galaxy and particularly from the sun, which will drown weak signals in the receiver. However, reduction in band-width and the use of codes reduces the effect of this noise, and in any case the foreseeable ranges of operation on a purely field-strength basis are already very great.

We can foresee the use of intermediate repeaters or relays. Such spacecraft would probably follow established orbits far out in the solar system and bordering on the limit of direct radio contact from the moon. Since they would also need to be tracking stations and beacons, these satellites would have to be extremely complex bodies.

The second problem concerns the time necessary for the propagation of radio signals over very great distances. In a telephone conversation, a transmission delay of even one second is intolerable. If a delay of 1,000 seconds each way for the transmission is acceptable, it will be possible to interrogate a spacecraft 300 million kilometres away from the base station. This is about twice the maximum distance from the earth to the sun. However, a total time of more than half an hour would elapse between question and response. In such circumstances, the crew of a manned space vehicle would need pretty strong nerves to withstand the loneliness of space, knowing that it would take half an hour for a simple, urgent message to be answered from base.

The distances I have mentioned are huge by present human

standards, but they are likely to be attained long before man has reached outside the solar system. While the mean distance of the earth from the sun is a little less than 150 million kilometres, the equivalent distance in the case of Saturn is 1,418 million kilometres and, in the case of Neptune, 4,469 million kilometres. Any space vehicle setting off for these regions will be gone a long time, and collecting information from it will be exceedingly difficult. When the transit time of signals becomes intolerable, due to distance, the radio engineer can offer no more miracles. There is no way of accelerating radio signals to speeds beyond the velocity of light.

Unknown Transmissions

One particular branch of communications theory will need to be expanded – that is, the basic theory of modulation. Modulation study so far has been largely related to the fact that modulation and demodulation are mirror images. Demodulation has been the process of extracting an already-known modulation form or forms from a given emission. But, in the exploration of space, the search for other intelligent life in the universe will go on, so that space vehicles should be equipped with devices for detecting whether or not a received radiation is deliberately modulated, even though the means or content of the modulation may be entirely new.

The International Telecommunication Union

Finally, if the various aspects of telecommunications in space exploration in 1984 are to be realized, many changes will have had to be made to the functions and structure of the International Telecommunication Union. It was perhaps too early for this at the ITU's 1963 Space Communication Conference, but it is clear that the basic differences between terrestrial and extra-terrestrial communications will demand different techniques. So long as space communications are operated on an earth-space-earth basis, the problem is not urgent, but once earth-space communications come to be channelled via the Moon Base we shall have to recognize two separate fields of activity. The ITU, which was organized in 1865 as the International Telegraph Union and whose first purpose is to maintain and extend international cooperation for the improvement and rational use of telecommunications of all kinds, will be very much concerned with developments in outer space. In particular, this international body will be needed to prevent incompatibilities and interference arising between space communications and terrestrial communications (including those which involve communication satellites) and to plan for the efficient development of these two aspects of telecommunication.

EXPLORATION TO THE FARTHEST PLANETS

by Dr Wernher von Braun

Director, George C. Marshall Space Flight Center, National Aeronautics and Space Administration, Huntsville, Alabama

Man may have landed on the surface of Mars by 1984. If not, he will surely have made a close approach for personal observation of the red planet. Likewise, manned 'fly-bys' to Venus will have been made.

Lunar landings will have long since passed from the fantastic achievement to routine occurrence. Astronauts will be shuttling back and forth on regular schedules from the earth to a small permanent base of operations on the moon. A part of the activity on the lunar surface may well be the operation of an astronomical observatory, taking advantage of the favourable observation conditions there.

Private industry will have entered earth-orbital operations on a large scale. Unmanned but heavily instrumented commercial telephone and television relay satellites carry messages and programmes across the oceans. Business firms, universities, and governments transmit myriads of technical data via satellite from computer to computer. Satellites are not much more numerous, but they are larger and more directly important to the well-being of the man in the street. Their operational life can be measured in dozens of years, and most can manoeuvre to maintain a desired orbit over extended periods.

Accurate long-range weather forecasts are available for any spot on the globe. Ships and aircraft use special satellites as navigational aids. Surveyors use others to provide geodetic fixes in inaccessible areas.

Saturn V, the largest launch vehicle under development in 1964 in America, will have been able, before 1970, to shove a payload of 100,000 pounds to earth-escape velocity. But for the manned exploration of Mars and the build-up of a sizeable lunar base, a vehicle is needed that will haul ten times as much payload, including men and their life-support equipment. That is why a launch rocket far more powerful than *Saturn V* is under development in 1984.

While chemical propulsion is still used for the first stage of large launch vehicles, improved engines and new fuels give higher specific impulse – more thrust per pound of fuel. Nuclear heat propulsion is used for upper stages, doubling the size of payloads that can be lifted free of the earth's gravity. The sustained low thrust and high fuel economy of nuclear-powered electric propulsion systems serves to push unmanned probes to the outermost planets of the solar system.

Instrumented payloads have been landed on some of the nearer planets. There may be one on one of Jupiter's satellites, and perhaps one on an asteroid, and they are busily sending back data on surface composition, atmospheric environment and the like. Investigations of the comets may have developed into a particularly fascinating chapter of unmanned interplanetary rocketry.

We shall be much nearer to the answer to the mystery of the origin of the solar system. The existence of a low order of life on Mars will probably have been proven, and the significance of the seasonal changes of the Martian canals established.

Manned orbiting space laboratories with closed ecological systems have supported pioneering crews comfortably in space for an uninterrupted stretch of two years. The hazard of particle radiation, in particular that posed by giant solar flares, has been eliminated with efficient new shielding methods. Fuel cells, solar and nuclear systems provide ample power for extended space flights and for surface operations on the moon. Men and women in space keep in constant touch with friends at home through effective communications, even when they are scores of millions of miles away.

Improved communications systems that link the earth with artificial satellites, the moon, and planets are based on light-signalling with the laser, whose transmission capability permits extended use of television for such long-distance communications. The laser is also incorporated in space radar systems, achieving an accuracy greater than the best radar in use in 1964.

Astronomically, the most important discoveries concerning the nature, extent, and origin of our universe will have been made by large telescopes based on the moon and by others revolving about the earth. In the visible region of the spectrum, these telescopes are taking full advantage of the fact that their performance is not impaired by the blur of any atmosphere. But the most important discoveries made with these instruments involve observations, recordings, and photographs in that vast area of the electro-magnetic spectrum for which the earth's atmosphere is opaque. Quite likely, some of these telescopes circling the earth will be established in twenty-four-hour orbits for ease of operations. Sitting apparently motionless up in the sky, at a fixed azimuth and elevation with respect to any given point on the earth's surface beneath, they will be aimed and controlled by armchair observers on the earth's surface, and some of them may be operated and maintained by technicians living in nearby orbiting laboratories.

Recovery and re-use of rocket boosters will be common, and will have greatly reduced the cost of a round-trip seat to orbit.

Instruments continue to be indispensable in the exploration of space. But man has proven himself irreplaceable as an explorer of the moon, and is getting ready to explore the rest of the solar system in person. A man's brain is still the ultimate in micro-miniaturization in size, weight, memory storage, and complex thinking operations. A large electronics computer might be superior at adding, subtracting, and in doing man's routine cleri-cal work. But, even in 1984, it remains for the brain of man to correlate unexpected observations, to perceive solutions to novel situations and to take independent action in the light of new data collected by his instruments. It is clear that man himself, and not just instruments, must explore the planets.

Gradually, space exploration has become a kind of standard behind which dynamic men with their courage, fighting instincts and talents have begun to rally for their advancement. Wars, which had somewhat similar 'rallying' effects, are no longer feas-ible between industrialized nations nor are they a suitable yard-stick for their strength – now that any military exchange with weapons of mass destruction would mean total annihilation of friend and foe alike.

Just as the Crusades saved Europe much bloodshed by diverting the energies of its fighting men to a far-away objective, so space exploration provides a worthwhile outlet for the pent-up energies of man in the late twentieth century. Until recently, huge defence programmes had provided much of the stimulus for research and development work without which industrial progress comes to a halt. In 1984, the limitless scientific and technological challenges of the space-exploration programme have taken over this vital, invigorating role. The 'spin-off' products of the space programme, direct or indirect, are visible everywhere.

More citizens of the world than ever before are taking part in the affairs of government. Well-informed, thinking men will continue to support this intriguing and profitable endeavour of space exploration. How far we go in space – and how fast – will continue to be affected by the measure of public support.

Exploration of the planets, and later of the stars, may not be the one and only peaceful force to pull man and his culture forward. But it is the only one I know (in 1964) in which all men can enjoy both the excitement of conquest and the technological, economic, and spiritual benefits. If mankind in 1984 is freer in thought and spirit, as well as politically and economically freer of the shackles of the environment, I firmly believe it will, in large measure, be thanks to the benefits of space exploration.

Natural Resources

MINERAL ORES: A CHALLENGE TO EUROPE

by Pierre Laffitte

École nationale supérieure des mines, Paris

By now world reserves of mineral ores and world demand do not present any serious problem. Taking the world as a whole, it is highly probable that by 1984 the situation will be much the same – with the exception, perhaps, of diamonds and of some substances of minor importance, which can easily be substituted. Many massive reports, a tremendous volume of publications, and the experience of recent years support this view.

Mineral resources are, however, very unequally distributed over the globe. At all times – and the Quest of the Golden Fleece and the search for the Cassiterides bear witness to their antiquity – prospecting for, and trade in, mineral ores has been an international matter. Until thirty or forty years ago, such prospecting and trade was confined mainly to the ores of great value. Recent falls in freight rates have, however, facilitated the transport of heavy ores. A Mauretanian or Brazilian iron ore deposit will, according to the economists, soon be just as well located (if not better) as a Lorraine or Swedish mine to serve the ports of Dunkirk or Genoa.

In the world of our time, the strategic importance of the mining industry, more consciously recognized during periods of political tension, has often been stressed. This emphasis on the importance of the industry is even more noticeable if we bear in mind that the turnover figures involved are relatively small. If we exclude coal, petroleum, water, and building materials, the whole of the mining and first conversion industry represents, in turnover, less than 1 per cent of the gross national product of an industrialized country. Yet if a small part of this 1 per cent is lacking, the economic machine stops!

From a geopolitical as from a political point of view, we may roughly divide the world in four: Europe, North America, the Soviet bloc, and the underdeveloped countries.

Europe still imports her raw materials from two main areas: North America and the Soviet bloc. The foreign trade of the U.S.A. and Russia was characterized by bulk exports of raw materials during the nineteenth century and part of the present century, but they then became importers from the remainder of the world. Two tendencies have developed in the under-developed countries: opposition to the exportation of crude ores, as this is (erroneously) considered an indirect form of the flight of national wealth, and a trend towards the creation, on the spot, of a first-conversion industry, or even the production of semi-manufactured goods.

Considering the speed with which world affairs change and develop through the centuries, the trading structure in the underdeveloped countries may alter very rapidly, and, by 1984, it will no doubt be difficult to import raw materials. The present situation of prosperity for the European consumer industries and of lean times for the mining industries will not last for long.

At the present time, producers and consumers throughout the world are engaged in competition of the fiercest kind. The violent fluctuations resulting from this state of affairs, the psychological and political repercussions (industrial and governmental stock-piling or dumping), the multiform aid of the governments to their respective mining industries, the uncertain attitudes of the U.S.S.R. and China make any medium-term forecasts hazardous, even if the long-term tendencies are known.

A large proportion of the new resources which European industry will have to utilize in 1984 will be found in Europe, in submerged deposits, non-outcropping deposits, and those of low content. To make use of these resources, the governments of Europe will have to support considerable scientific research. I believe that only in this way will European industry be able to retain that degree of economic security essential for the future.

Fundamental research in geology and mineralogy

If the kind of deposits just mentioned are to be found, great progress will have to be made in the sciences of metallogenesis. The various branches of the geological and mineralogical sciences, petrology, geochemistry, sedimentology, and tectonics, are also involved. But I must stress the importance which should be attached to documentation, in the form of a more intensive effort in metallogenic cartography, geostatistics, and the rational study of the distribution of mineral wealth throughout the world. Included in this descriptive literature, of course, must be the study of the origin of deposits by field and laboratory methods, mineral syntheses, thermometric and manometric geological studies, natural isotopic fractionation, etc. It will be advisable, in this connexion, to resume and develop the studies which will promote the knowledge of thermodynamics and of the natural sciences in this field which, to use L. de Launay's phrase, may be described as 'natural metallurgy'.

Methods of prospecting

Geological and metallogenic studies form only a part, however, of what has to be developed, to reach objectives such as those of submarine deposits or non-outcropping deposits. The methods of prospecting, whether direct or indirect, must also form part of the scientific research and technical improvement. It is hazardous to separate the introduction of new methods from daily experience in prospecting, at least if this is done with an eye to technical progress. The mining industry itself takes a considerable interest in this matter and is anxious to see some improvement in the methods adopted for prospecting. Moreover, practical use may quickly be made of the results of such studies, if of course the effort in diffusion and publication is sufficient.

Operational methods in the mines

Taken as a whole, the processes involved in mining, from the rock on site to the ore-washing head, are very costly and they constitute virtually the whole cost of mining. The use of mechanical means, by explosives, to break the rocks – often very badly – is not necessarily the only solution to the problem. And we can mention here only a few of the studies of the various characteristics required: compressibility, brittleness, elasticity, the coefficients of thermal or electrical conduction of rock ores, and the study of the interactions of various forms of mechanical, thermal, electrical, and electromagnetic energy with the minerals.

It is no exaggeration to say that these fields of research have received but scant attention and that all the difficulties (or the facility) which will be found, from laboratory observation to application in the mining industry, are still unknown. A programme of research into rock mechanics will have to be prepared on a vast scale and bold efforts must be made to open up new fields of inquiry. When we consider the number of engineers engaged in the development of the industries using mined products, thousands of top-level research workers will be required in these neglected fields in Europe in 1984. Urgent action must be taken, therefore, to ensure that, by that time, the many young scientists are not just beginners.

Although the study of milling plants has not been neglected, it is nevertheless worthy of further consideration. The financial means for research are too small, where the preparation of ores by mechanical or chemical processes is concerned. The same applies to biological preparation, where we are still at an elementary stage. In the field of metallurgical preparation, an exhaustive study has yet to be made of high-temperature phenomena. Progress in each branch of technique extends the number of processes and their importance, thus widening the range of use of the workable ores.

The problem of underground milling is worthy of considerable thought. It does not seem satisfactory to spend a great deal of human labour and effort to bring to the surface material containing 90 to 99 per cent 'sterile' rock. Has a really deep scientific and economic study been made of the construction of miniature transportable washeries for underground use ? And have many other methods been tried ? In the mine of the future we shall use kilowatts, calories, natural gases, or other ingredients – perhaps with underground crushing, perhaps with the use of magnetic or electrical fields, whence we shall remove anode plates, slag, or other concentrates. In 1964 this is science fiction. But all this will be possible for the mining industry of 1984.

High-pressure and high-temperature operation in the chemical industry is very costly. In the mining industry, on the other hand, bearing in mind that the rock may constitute a well-tried wall, such cost may be very low. Is not this an advantage ? There is another advantage: the cubic kilometre of space and endurance of systems for many years of time, unfamiliar in the activities of the physicist and the chemist, are commonplace to the geologist and the miner.

It appears rather hypothetical to believe that small and overcrowded Europe, the cradle of industrial civilization, can develop her mineral resources to such an extent that she will be in a position to face the increasing difficulties of supply. But it is not impossible. French successes during the past twenty years, in the fields of uranium and petroleum, clearly demonstrate that, when one joins determination and finance, the results quickly and profitably follow. The drive for technical progress, given the will for future independence, can enable European industry to continue to illumine the rest of our planet.

LEARNING THE VALUE OF WATER

by Michel Batisse

Chief, Natural Resources Research Division, U.N.E.S.C.O., Paris

For anyone who has lived in the desert, the value of water is very clear. But for the many of us who enjoy the amenities of modern civilization, water is a commodity pretty much taken for granted. We easily accept the idea that there is no substitute for it in its many uses. We do not, however, appreciate how much of it is required and how much we depend on its availability, not only in our homes, but also for growing crops or for making steel or paper.

Leaving aside the need for hydro-electric power production, for inland navigation, and for recreation, where no significant withdrawal or pollution of water is involved, the amount of water used, *per capita*, for domestic, industrial and agricultural purposes varies enormously from country to country. It ranges, at present, from 10 gallons per day in some underdeveloped areas to the impressive figure of 1,800 gallons per day in the United States, where only 6 per cent of this is for domestic uses, the rest being shared by industry and agriculture.

A very important distinction must, however, be made between water which is actually consumed (that is, returned to the atmosphere in the form of vapour) and that which ultimately finds its way back – more or less polluted – to a river or infiltrates into the ground, and can therefore eventually be used again. Irrigation is a typical example of a highly consumptive use. Some 60 per cent of the water diverted for irrigation purposes evaporates from canals or from the soil or is transpired through plants. On the other hand, cooling for industry, although using very large quantities of water, is typical of a non-consumptive use.

Let us now consider what the water needs are likely to be in 1984, in comparison with today, in spite of the fact that very few reliable data are available on the subject.

The demand for domestic use will increase proportionally to the population increase – that is, by at least 50 per cent. However, it will also increase with the raising of standards of living, so that a doubling by 1984 of worldwide domestic requirements for water seems a conservative estimate.

A very sharp increase in the water demand for industrial purposes is clearly to be anticipated everywhere during the coming years. The larger part of this water will be required for condensers and for cooling, and, as little pollution results, re-use of the water is possible. But the main problem lies with the many and rapidly expanding industries such as chemicals, rubber, petroleum refining, etc., which not only use large quantities of water but also produce heavy pollution. The uncertainty of changing economic factors, which may lead to important changes in industrial uses of water, makes it difficult to foresee clearly the future requirements in this field. But, again, it seems that a doubling of the total world requirement would constitute a very conservative estimate.

The situation with respect to agriculture, essentially irrigation, shows conflicting trends. On the one hand, with an increasing scarcity of water leading to higher prices in certain areas, such a highly consumptive use as irrigation may become less favoured. On the other hand, however, the pressing need for food in the underdeveloped world, together with the high yields obtained in areas of intense solar radiation, should lead to a great increase in irrigated areas. And even in humid temperate countries like Britain, the practice of supplementary irrigation will be introduced. Here again, judging from the trends in recent years, an increase of as much as 100 per cent in world demands for agriculture does not seem unrealistic.

Altogether, the total demand for water in the world will therefore approximately double between now and 1984. As against this, it is clear that the natural supply, which comes from precipitation, will be approximately the same as now. In fact, we are far from having a clear picture of the water balance and resources in the various countries or basins. There is controversy on exactly how much of the rainfall reaches the rivers or the groundwater aquifers, on the amount of evapotranspiration which takes place and on the volume and processes of replenishment of aquifers. By 1975, however, the results of the International Hydrological Decade – which will start in 1965 – will have clarified many of these points and given a sound basis for evaluating the resources and for analysing the effects of man's interference in the hydrological cycle.

In 1984, the total natural supply of water, a crude measure of which is given by the total streamflow, will still be many times larger than the demand. But this supply is not now and will not then be properly distributed either in location or in time. The enormous surplus of the Amazon River will still be of little use to other countries, and long-distance transport of water will be as expensive as it is now. Similarly, storage of flood water to spread out variability of river flow in time will still be limited by the economic consideration of diminishing returns in building larger structures. Thus, the dependable supply where and when needed will still be substantially less than the total natural supply. Although the margin between needs and resources will still be comfortable in many areas, there will be an increasing number of situations of water scarcity.

In order to adapt the dependable supply of doubling needs, it is clear that considerable development in the water field will be required everywhere. The magnitude of the problem can hardly be over-estimated and a number of means will have to be employed to meet the situation.

Efforts will first be made to limit the increase in consumptive use. In the United States, for instance, although the total water use will double, consumptive use, which at present is in the vicinity of 100,000 million gallons per day, is not expected to reach more than 170,000 million gallons per day in twenty years' time. This prediction, however, is based on an anticipated relative reduction in the role of irrigation which cannot be foreseen else-where. Reducing evaporation on large reservoirs in arid climates, like Aswan, will not save very great amounts. Similarly, no large increase in total water supply can be anticipated from a reduction of natural evapotranspiration through land and vegetation management.

The re-use of water coming from industries and also from sewage will be far more important than now, especially in such cases as those of the Rhine or the Ohio River. This will imply a much stronger control of pollution through expensive water-treatment processes. As regards drainage waters coming from irrigation, they are normally too rich in dissolved salts to be used a second time.

Groundwater (i.e. underground) reserves are enormous all over the world. They are very slowly replenished, but they can be 'mined', as long as it remains economical to do so, using the capital rather than the interest. There is nothing basically wrong in doing this as long as everybody is aware of the consequences, including a progressive lowering of water levels in aquifers and increasing cost of pumping.

What about the possibilities of increasing the supply through other means? In some cases, in arid areas, irrigation water with higher salt content may be tolerated by plants through improved practices. The possibility of increasing rainfall artificially may assist in filling reservoirs in mountainous areas, but will play no significant role in the total picture. And the melting of large parts of the icecaps belongs to the world of science fiction.

It seems probable, therefore, that the only 'new' source of water which will begin to be of significance in 1984 will come from the desalting either of sea water (through processes of distillation or freezing) or of brackish water (through electro-dialysis). Water produced in combination with electricity in large-scale plants – probably with nuclear power – is likely to become competitive for domestic and industrial purposes in many places. Although perhaps not yet very important in the total water picture, desalinization will become a growing feature of the future.

A number of important consequences will result from the mag-nitude of the water problems to be managed. The necessity for large-scale and long-term planning at river-basin level, at country level, and even at continental level, with due consideration of hydrological phenomena and of alternative uses of water, will become more and more clear. Such enterprises as the Mekong River scheme in south-east Asia are the first signs of this tendency. Techniques of analysis will have to be further developed to weigh the relative merits of using water for industry versus irrigation or recreation, from both an economical and a social point of view. The choices made will have considerable impact, in particular in the development of the arid lands. The availability and cost of water will become a major element in development planning.

On the financial side, the figures involved in doubling the amount of water for world supply in twenty years are enormous. They may reach £1 million million. The ratepayer, particularly in large cities, will be faced with heavy bills for more and more complex works for water transportation and storage or for its treatment and quality control.

As a result, there will be many progressive changes in our habits of thinking about water, about its value, about the interrelation between its uses, about the interdependence of the people living in the same basins with all the legal and political implications this involves. There will be no shortage of water. It will just cost more. And man will begin to realize clearly how much he depends on it. This will not be new in history, since the ancient Egyptians, the Romans and the Arabs knew the value of water. But for the first time, and for ever, modern civilization will become water-conscious.

A NEW BALANCE BETWEEN MAN AND NATURE

by Professor François Bourlière

President, International Union for Conservation of Nature and Natural Resources

The rapid increase in the populations of the various countries of the world, the continued development of lands previously un-cultivated, in order to provide food, and the progressive industrial-ization of most of the previously underdeveloped countries – these trends may make us fear a radical transformation within the next twenty years in all these countries, with a gradual replacement of wild life by cultivated plants and domestic animals. In short, we may see man monopolizing the biological production of the earth's surface solely for his own benefit – such a monopoly being created at the expense of wild life. There are, indeed, some pessimists who foretell the approaching extinction of what little remains of the big game in Africa or elsewhere, and the complete replacement, very soon, of all the natural forests by the planting of trees which grow more quickly and produce more wood or pulp than the wild species. Others predict the general pollution of the water and the air.

Some of their fears are, unfortunately, quite well founded. Nevertheless, it is irrational and dangerous to suppose that man is in out-and-out opposition to nature, or to consider that the unquestionable predominance of our species in the biosphere of today and of tomorrow must necessarily be accompanied by the total destruction of wild plants and animals. The inference is that man can override nature, that he is quite capable of living all his life in a world of concrete and steel, without feeling the need to escape from it, and that every plant and every animal is necessarily a competitor or an adversary – in other words, that the success of humanity must involve the disappearance of all the natural ecosystems. Nothing seems so unsafe to affirm; indeed it would appear that men are becoming increasingly aware of the dangers in all scientifically and technically advanced countries.

It seems, in fact, that, for a variety of reasons, there is a place for nature everywhere where man operates, if only for the sake of his own physical and psychical make-up. If those responsible for economic development and for the material and moral wellbeing of the nations really wish to take into account the recent developments in applied ecology and to implement the policy of rational conservation of natural resources which follows, a new balance between man and nature will be struck during the next twenty years – a balance from which both should benefit.

The chaotic development of the great industrial centres we have witnessed during the past half century cannot, in fact, continue. The megalopolies which have been created and which are growing in almost all parts of the world have reached a point at which they constitute a greater and greater threat to man, who finds it extremely difficult to adapt himself to them. These densely populated areas, with their highly strained rhythm of life, the extreme specialization of human activities, and the multiplicity of pollutions of all kinds, have led to an ever-increasing number of the 'diseases of civilization' which, each year, are creating new problems for those responsible for the health and welfare of nations. What we have gained in a century of medical discoveries and of improvement in the standard of living, we are on the brink of losing, in the form of premature ageing of some of our functions, or through psychical disturbances of varying nature.

The antidote to this *mal du siècle* is not only to be found in the discovery of new tranquillizers or in research into new methods of treatment of arterio-sclerosis. It is also, and pre-eminently, to be found in the achievement of a better balance of psychical and physical activities, in the periodical escape from the crowds in the big cities, and in the expansion of the green belts and recreation areas.

The industrial agglomerations of 1984 will thus have to include numerous parks and, above all, there will be 'social forests' surrounding them (they are already being so called in some quarters), with relaxation and rest areas – natural oases where a number of wild plants and animals will be able to exist in the vicinity of the towns. In such a way man – himself the most precious natural resource to conserve in urban areas – will be able to coexist peacefully with some remnants of undomesticated Nature, for the benefit of both. It is only by such means that our children will really be able to enjoy, tomorrow, the fruits of the scientific and technical developments of today.

In all the agricultural areas endowed with rich soil and intense biological activity, in both tropical latitudes and temperate climes, the world of 1984 will certainly leave but little place for wild life. The mechanization of agriculture and the large-scale use of herbicides and insecticides will lead to a total monopoly of Man on plant and animal productivity. Rich soils will therefore be turned into gigantic 'calorie factories' with little space left for untamed Nature.

All wild life will, in such activities, certainly be considered as competitive with man and therefore destined to extermination.

There will be only, here and there, a few natural reserves kept for scientific or aesthetic reasons. But these will be mere ecological islets, isolated examples in the midst of a hostile world, and such reserves, like the animals which find refuge there, will have to be carefully managed, to avoid the risks inherent in overpopulation. Provided they be sufficient in number, and ecologically self-supporting, forming a network within the same continent, such reserves should nevertheless ensure the survival of reasonably large samples, not only of resident animal species, but also of migratory birds.

The experience of the past few decades has shown us that mechanized agriculture and intensive stock-farming develop principally in areas with rich soil and a favourable climate. It is here and only here that the investment of large sums in the modernization of agriculture or the great plans for development is likely to prove profitable. On the contrary, the poor farming areas, and the areas which are scarcely cultivable, gradually lose their inhabitants and are abandoned by *Homo economicus*. Here, then, is the great opportunity for the wild life of tomorrow.

The areas where intensive development is hardly possible are numerous indeed in all parts of the world, and they are to be found in every latitude and in every continent. There are some even in densely populated Europe – mountainous regions, tundras, and some Mediterranean islands, for example. In the tropics, many of the savannas and desert areas are similarly placed. In these regions, the creation of natural refuges is easier, provided the necessary funds are forthcoming for their maintenance. A glance at the list of national parks and equivalent reserves will suffice to show that most of them are already situated in regions of this type.

It is highly probable that, in 1984, nearly all the surviving wild life on the globe will have taken refuge in such reserves. Our generation therefore has the duty to ensure that a sufficiently large sample of each natural eco-system on our globe should be represented in this worldwide network of reserves, which will constitute also the open-air laboratories of the ecologists and ethologists of tomorrow. These reserves will in fact be the 'reference laboratories' for the objective assessment of the long-term value of development schemes.

Moreover, many of these parks can be open, at least in part, to tourists, and they will be a source of considerable income to many countries which are not so favoured with other natural resources. In 1964 it takes already but a few hours to fly from Europe to Central and to East Africa to admire the magnificent wild life to be found there. At the moment, those who travel abroad each year may be counted in their tens of thousands, but it is by no means improbable that by 1984 these numbers will be multiplied by ten or even a hundred.

In the temperate zones of Eurasia or in North America, there are millions of visitors already – fishermen, game-shooters, or those who travel simply to enjoy the fresh air, anxious to get away for a few weeks into a smoke-free, petrol-free atmosphere, to fly from the sight of factory chimneys, or even just to enjoy a quiet night's sleep. They will be followed, in 1984, by tens of millions of people doing the same thing, and this will mean that the recreation areas and national parks will have an adequate income, bringing life and prosperity to numerous regions which might otherwise have remained permanently impoverished.

It is therefore not inevitable that, by 1984, nature will have become entirely domesticated, artificial, standardized, and devoid of interest. Nor is it indispensable that our children be reduced to the state in which they have to take pills from time to time, to reduce their fecundity, adjust their temperaments, be able to sleep, or try to find that life still has a meaning for them. There is, however, no time to lose. The conservationists must rise above the 'emotional' or purely zoological or botanical state they have so far cultivated. They must share their experiences and combine their efforts with the agriculturalists, the town-planners, the welfare workers, and the economists. Nature will not be saved against man, but with his cooperation and for his own sake.

ORCHESTRATING THE USE OF LAND

by E. M. Nicholson

Director-General, The Nature Conservancy, London

After long neglect and maltreatment the environment which shelters, supports, and inspires us is coming to be looked at with new interest and respect. Partly through sheer pressure of expanding population, partly through higher living standards and increased mobility, and partly through the dubious gift conferred by our technology of being able to make bigger mistakes oftener, land use is fast becoming a major public issue.

Among our natural resources, minerals are the most localized and strictly defined, wild life the most vulnerable, water the most underrated, and land the most complex and confusing. In 1984, people will reflect with astonishment that in close on 900 years since *Domesday Book* it needed all but the final decade or so before government and people began to think at all coherently of land as having serious economic values in terms other than crops and livestock.

The coming revolution in outlook will have sprung from a number of sources. Ever more rapid changes in land use, and more frequent issues needing decision between rival uses, will require probably annual or biennial revisions of a wide range of maps dealing on different scales with such aspects as land use generally, zoning and other restrictions, buildings by classes, communications, daily and seasonal movements, and rates of change. Much increased use of photogrammetry, and new cartographic techniques, will assist in the supply of maps, but more significant will be the growth of a sizeable professional body of map analysts from the ranks of biologists, geologists, soil scientists, and optical physicists, elaborately equipped to trace complex and subtle correlations and to present (wherever necessary in map form) the implications of sets of alternative choices. Soils will be studied more as a whole, for instance, throughout their whole depth as well as superficially in relation to agricultural production. Pedology, the science of the study of soils, will be given added impetus as the need for the amelioration and conservation of the more difficult soils of the world increases.

Many choices will originate from detailed mapping of soils and intensive investigations of such soil properties as structure, fertility, biological activity, and moisture capacity. Accurate evaluation of the possibilities for soil improvement will be more feasible, so that the cost of remedying any water, mineral, or biological deficiencies can be clearly stated. The role of plants and animals of certain species in improving soil fertility will be better understood, as will be the manifold factors causing rapid breakdown of organic matter and its incorporation into the mineral soil so that the capital of plant nutrients may be readily available.

Foresters will have worked out more precisely the types of forest to establish on different soils to give the greatest sustained yield, and the species of trees used will have been specially bred for this purpose. Many of the present agricultural and forestry practices will be outdated by new techniques designed to combine soil improvement and long-term immunity to pests, diseases, and windthrow without jeopardizing maximum amenity and landscape values. More will be known of the best siting and type of hedgerows and windbreaks in different regions to ensure they provide the greatest benefit to man.

High priority will be given to the rehabilitation, often at heavy cost, of land rendered derelict by dumping of industrial spoil, grossly excessive application of persistent toxic chemicals for agricultural or other purposes, and failure to restore topsoil and suitable grades and levels after extractive operations. Deeper understanding of the dynamics of soil-forming processes will enable us to control more effectively not only natural processes in soils but those which are artificial and damaging. Furthermore, man will be able to produce soils of his own making without waiting thousands of years for normal soil-forming processes. The cost of doing this will be initially, in economic terms, astronomical, but will eventually be so cheapened that production of food in the more difficult regions of the world will be a practical proposition.

In these and other ways, practices and attitudes will develop of considering critically what is and what might be in every area of land use. The rejection of present-day oscillations, between taking inherited patterns for granted and embarking on often discordant and short-sighted piecemeal changes, will also require the development of new tools in the social sciences. Economists will be compelled to acquire greater technological knowledge and to devise more sophisticated means of following through the long-range implications of alternative courses in investment and provision of facilities, particularly where possibilities of multi-purpose use are important, as in the case of reservoirs

suitable for waterside or aquatic recreations, or where tourist
revenues and increases in property and rateable values are
involved.

Much more importance will attach to predicting and guarding
against the characteristic adverse impacts on land of different
types of human user, whether they are engaged in cropping it of
renewable resources, extracting non-renewable resources, taking
it for a building site or using it as an arena for some outdoor
activity. While the importance of town and country planning will
remain and indeed increase, much of its current restrictive or
didactic flavour will fade out as land users become more deeply
and vividly aware of themselves as playing one of many roles in a
drama whose form is determined more and more clearly by the
requirements of the land itself as a continuing habitat for
mankind.

The planner, equipped with a more hybrid training in natural
and social science, will become less the referee blowing the
whistle and more the conductor of a tolerably well-rehearsed
orchestra, which will tend to be on a regional rather than a local
pattern. Landowners, land-users, and the land-linked professions,
including forestry, agriculture, estate management, and land
agency and landscape design (now called landscape architecture)
will be in continuous liaison with land planning through flexible
codes frequently revised as new knowledge can be built into them
from a greatly increased programme of environmental research.
This research will also largely form the base for a substantial
common element in the training and retraining of members of all
the vocations and professions concerned with the land, and this
again will make for a new degree of integration of attitudes and
adaptability to new ideas and requirements.

Out of all this will emerge a new relation between land and
leisure. People will go to see and criticize and enjoy special land-
scapes, as they now go to see architectural works, and they will
expect and welcome new experiments and techniques in landscape
design, especially in connexion with the great works of civil
engineering, which by then will be already dwarfing anything yet
seen on the earth. In few fields is the impact of research likely to be
more far-reaching; or more formative of the future pattern of
our civilization.

Food and Agriculture

THE RACE WILL NOT YET BE WON

by Dr B. R. Sen

Director-General, Food and Agriculture Organization of the United Nations, Rome

Twenty years may seem a short enough time measured against the development of world agriculture. Yet the next two decades must see a period of development unprecedented in the terms of past progress. In whole continents of the world and in a host of countries the technique of agriculture is undergoing a revolution – a revolution not so much of new techniques (as were the industrial revolutions of the nineteenth century in what are now the developed regions of the world), but a revolution in the sense that known techniques long held back by a variety of political and social barriers are now being made available in less developed parts of the world.

We now see large populations eking out an existence subject to the vagaries of climate and season, burdened occasionally by famine and continually by malnutrition. We also see them expanding at an unprecedented rate.

This expansion of population is the continuation of a trend which is stimulated as living conditions improve throughout the world. For every seven persons in the world twenty years ago there are now ten and, on conservative estimates, there will be sixteen in 1984. These changes are even more striking in the less-developed regions of the world (the far East, Mainland China, the Near East, Africa, and Latin America excluding the River Plate countries). In these regions, for every ten persons alive today it is estimated that there will be seventeen in 1984. These regions will account for three quarters of the world population in 1984.

Thus, without any improvement in the existing level of diet there will need to be an overall increase of 57 per cent in the level of food supplies in the world as a whole by 1984 and of 68 per cent in the less-developed regions.

These are big increases and emphasize the pressure to change which is evident throughout the developing countries of the world today, yet they allow for no improvement in existing diets. In FAO's *Third World Food Survey* we have formulated targets based on nutritional needs. These targets imply that there should be an increase of about one third in the total food supply of the less-developed regions of the world in order to satisfy current needs.

Taking into account both population changes and the need to improve existing diets, the total food supplies of the less-developed regions of the world need to be *two and a quarter times* their existing level by 1984. This increase is in total food supply. The supply of foods of animal origin in the less-developed regions of the world would need to be increased to *three times* their existing level. For the world as a whole by 1984, total food supplies would need to be *one and three quarter* times the existing level and animal foods *nearly doubled*.

This then is the likely world food requirement in 1984. To what extent can world agricultural production meet the task that lies before it ? There is little doubt that technically on a worldwide scale these increases can be achieved. It has been estimated that, without any expansion of the world's cultivated area, production of crops could be doubled and that of livestock products increased fivefold. Only 10 per cent of the world's land surface is cultivated at present. Much of the remainder is either too dry, too mountainous, or too cold for normal cultivation. But some expansion of the cultivated land is possible. Agricultural resources can also be supplemented by a very great increase in the production of fish.

How far in practice will mankind be able to utilize existing technical knowledge to achieve the essential increase in food production ? This is a difficult question to answer. Nothing could be more misleading than to assess trends in agricultural production and to extrapolate them into the future. Any forecast of this nature must take into account the changing attitudes and aspirations of the people. The developing countries are becoming increasingly aware of their appallingly low level of living and the need to improve it through planned development. The aim of FAO's Freedom from Hunger Campaign has been to aid the countries in this task of combating hunger and malnutrition and of breaking the vicious circle of low levels of food consumption, productivity, and income.

The factors which must be considered in estimating what may be achieved can be grouped under three broad headings: (1) the effect of technical progress on crop and livestock yields; (2) the effect of rising population on the intensity of cultivation which in turn affects crop and livestock yields; and (3) the possibility of increasing production through the development of new land resources.

As regards technical progress, the advantage seems to lie mainly with the densely settled areas which generally offer more favourable conditions for the application of many of the new techniques suitable for increasing production. We could think it not unreasonable to expect a simple annual rate of increase in production of 1·75 per cent in the densely populated areas of the Far East by the application of improved techniques on the existing agricultural land. Relatively smaller increases may be expected in the less densely populated areas. We have assumed rates of 1·25 per cent in the Near East, 1 per cent in Latin America, and 0·75 per cent in Africa.

More problematic is the assessment of the likely effect of rising population on food production in areas where a large proportion of the population lives on and by the land. With rising populations, in these circumstances, even with no increase in cultivated areas and no technical progress, production tends to increase with the natural evolution of a more intensive use of available agricultural resources, resulting in increasing yields. There is clearly more room for this intensification without technical progress in the emptier regions of Latin America and Africa than in the Far East where land resources are being used more intensively already, or in the Near East where the lack of water is a severely limiting factor. From the limited information available we have assumed 'elasticities' of 0·7 for Africa and Latin America and 0·3 for the Far East and Near East for the proportionate effect of rising population on production. The effects of technical progress and rising population on production are not independent. The joint effect of the two is also taken into account in our calculations.

As regards the third factor, the scope for extending the agricultural land is naturally largest in the least densely populated areas. It should be possible to achieve simple annual rates of increase in production as a result of developing new land resources of 1·5 per cent in Africa and Latin America, against only 0·25 per cent in the Far East and the Near East.

For the developed regions, we have assumed in our calculations straight rates of increase on the basis of past trends.

On the assumptions we have made, production in the developed countries can rise by 60 per cent by 1984 and thus exceed food needs which, on the basis of trends in population and income, are likely to rise by 30 per cent. For the less-developed regions taken as a group, the reverse picture obtains: with considerable effort, production might rise by 1984 by 85 per cent, though food needs – so defined as to take into account population increase and modest quantitative and qualitative improvements in the diets – will have risen by around 120 per cent. These broad estimates assume that, in the short interval to 1984, population policies will not have had time to be effective.

These figures conceal a wide variety of conditions. Thus, in the Far East where the heart of the world food problem lies, and in the Near East, production will probably fail to meet needs. Production and needs are expected to be more or less the same in Africa, and there is an expected excess of production over need in Latin America. On a worldwide scale, production is more or less equal to needs. If food deficiencies and surpluses are to be levelled out, food trade from the developed to the developing countries should amount to some 10 per cent of the world food production in 1984.

In the Far East and Near East the increase in agricultural production will demand a drastic change in techniques and major intensification. But even in Latin America and Africa which have greater margins of developing new land resources, dramatic efforts must be made towards reorganizing agricultural production, shifting from traditional subsistence to more effective agriculture, planning better land use, and relating nutritional policies to developmental efforts. Furthermore, the extent to which the best use is made of available resources will depend very much on the measures taken to improve the conditions of trade for the developing countries. In this respect, while the developing countries can improve their relative position somewhat by greater coordination in planning, real improvement will depend on the policies adopted by the developed countries.

Thus FAO, as well as other specialized agencies and groups interested in the problem, including the governments and peoples of the developing countries themselves, are faced with a most difficult dual task. There is not only the problem of increasing the productivity of agriculture in the developing nations through the spread and application of technical knowledge but also an equally pressing need for attention to problems of world trade in agricultural products. In fact, the actual situation with respect to food and agriculture in 1984 will depend in large part on whether we can create and maintain a sufficient awareness of the problem of world hunger to see that the necessary attention is given to these two tasks. They must be accomplished if large portions of mankind are not to face famine and starvation by 1984.

FARMING AS A SCIENCE-BASED INDUSTRY

by Sir William Slater, F.R.S.

Formerly Secretary, Agricultural Research Council, London

Although agriculture will be hard-pressed to feed the many people in the world in 1984, even at the present low levels, in Britain and other European countries the increased need will not be nearly so great as for the world as a whole; the anticipated rise in population is less and the initial standard of living already high. Unlike many parts of the world, however, Britain has little or no waste land to bring into cultivation. Instead, the farms must lose land needed for housing, factories, schools, offices, and roads. Another loss from the farms will be labour.

The British farmer will have to produce more on less land and with fewer men. To do so he will have to use every tool placed at his disposal by the scientist and technologist – or condemn himself to a life of slavery on an income providing a bare subsistence. There will always be some men prepared to follow this life from their love of the traditional ways on the land, but they will be in continuous danger of extinction and their numbers will undoubtedly have fallen by 1984. These farms will be family farms as the traditional methods will not allow hired labour at the wage levels agriculture must pay to keep abreast with a general rise in productivity.

For the rest of the land the management must, by 1984, have passed into the hands of men capable of applying every branch of science and technology, including modern techniques of management. Their farms must necessarily be of a size which will justify their ability, skill, and energy and bring them a reward sufficient to attract them from other industries anxious to buy their services. These farms will also be big enough to employ men with special skills rather than the all-round farm craftsman. These specialist workers will be needed to implement the decisions of scientific management. Farming will be a business with a major role to play in the nation's economy and, as such, the farmer will need the same control over his land as the industrial manager has over his factory floor.

On the arable land the cultivations will be increasingly mechanized, the management and operation of the machines being the responsibility of one group of workers. Field sizes will have been reshaped and enlarged to make cultivations easier, with the elimination of many of the hedgerows. Weeds will be almost entirely controlled by means of herbicides. Crop varieties bred to meet the needs of mechanized farming will be used exclusively. The use of fertilizers will be heavy but controlled. It will be essential to get the maximum economic yield, but equally important not to use unnecessarily heavy dressings; this may involve, in many instances, some form of laboratory control. The crops will be protected against pests and diseases, from seed time to harvest, largely by insecticides and fungicides. These will have been improved in selectivity and reduced in toxicity to species other than those it is desired to kill.

Farm stock will have to be equally productive. Breeding will, during the next twenty years, become more and more scientific. Already we are seeing the results of the work of the geneticists in the poultry industry, and the breeding of dairy cattle is rapidly following on similar lines. No longer will individual skill and judgement be enough; the farmer in 1984 will need the maximum degree of certainty in the productivity of his stock.

Another factor may have been introduced by 1984. Breeding has so far been concentrated on yield in quantity and nutritional quality – often at the expense of flavour. As the purely economic factors are satisfied there may arise a greater demand for food which not only nourishes the body but also pleases the palate.

The feeding of animals will be based on the growing knowledge of animal nutrition. Computers will formulate balanced rations for pigs and poultry at minimum cost, the protein being partly supplied by the mechanical breakdown of plant cells or by material synthesized by micro-organisms. The management of animals will be the work of men specially qualified. Every device to save labour while freeing the stockman to exercise his skill and powers of observation will be used. Animals are individuals and need individual attention, but that does not mean back-breaking labour. The less the stockman has to lift and haul the more care he can give to his animals. The design of buildings and the planning of the stock yard will be increasingly studied. It will be considered that 75 dairy cows should be a minimum herd size for one cowman.

There will be increased control of animal diseases, in particular the metabolic diseases, as our knowledge of animal physiology and pathology grows. More and more veterinary medicine will become preventive rather than curative. The veterinarian will attend on a fixed fee to watch over the animals continuously, and not be called in only when they are sick. Some successes may have been achieved in increasing yields by stimulating or changing in some other way the normal metabolism of the animal, but these are unlikely to compare in their effects with the straightforward improvements in stock management and hygiene.

There will be major changes in marketing by 1984. The large distributors will call for greater uniformity in the product, and more and more farm produce will pass through some form of processing and packaging. Markets to which produce comes in an unregulated flow, to pass either direct or through wholesalers to a large number of individual shops, will decline during the next twenty years. In their place will come arrangements whereby a standard product passes direct to a processer, who may either pack the product for distribution direct or process it for later sales.

Many of the larger farmers will combine to handle their own produce in this way.

What has been said of Britain will apply to most other developed countries. In the less-developed countries the pattern will be different. With an excess of manpower and an acute shortage of capital, their development in the next twenty years will depend on the education of the peasant farmer. Many of these countries can also increase the land under cultivation. They start with a primitive agriculture and, by the relatively modest use of fertilizer, by the control of pests and diseases and by suitable irrigation, they can double their crop yields by 1984; similarly, by the elimination of unprofitable animals, controlled grazing, and stamping out the major diseases, their output of animal products can be greatly raised.

A useful start should have been made in this direction by 1984, sufficient at least to match their rapidly growing population and to improve their poor diets. The technical problems are not difficult to solve. Whether the agriculture of the less-developed countries reaches the required levels by 1984 depends on the willingness of these countries to adopt economic and social changes and on the extent to which the more-developed countries are prepared to help them.

If, by 1984, the less-developed countries can double their agricultural output, they will be ready to move into a more advanced form of agriculture with larger units and mechanization in the remaining years of the century, and so meet the needs of the greater population increase which is expected by A.D. 2000.

BEWARE THE MALNUTRITION OF AFFLUENCE

by Professor John Yudkin

Department of Nutrition, Queen Elizabeth College, London

One thing is certain about the food of the future. In spite of the almost universal belief that we shall sooner or later be eating pills, we shall in fact have to eat the sorts of foods which need a plate, knife, fork, and spoon. The amount of protein, fat, and carbohydrate which our bodies need each day, with its mineral elements and vitamins, even if pure and dry, weighs something like one pound. This would make up a hundred or so quite large pills, and I doubt whether this is quite what people have in mind when they imagine food in this form.

On the contrary, what is becoming more and more clear is that people will only eat food which is palatable to them – food which is pleasant to look at, to smell, to taste, and to chew. And indeed it is within this context that, before 1984, we shall have deliberately to make changes in our food if we are to escape considerable hazard to our health. For the food manufacturer, with all the resources of science and technology, is increasingly able to make attractive foods, with tastes, colours, and textures which we find increasingly irresistible, but which may be nutritionally useless or even undesirable.

The qualities which attract us to our food are normally found together with its nutritional qualities, but are not identical with them. The texture and taste of meat has little to do with its protein or B vitamins, nor the texture and taste of fruit with its Vitamin C and its mineral elements. Left to ourselves, we are today eating large and increasing amounts of sugar, mostly in a range of highly attractive manufactured foods. Tomorrow, we may be eating savoury foods with perhaps an even greater attractiveness than meat, but with none of its nutritional qualities.

We cannot blame the food manufacturer for making our foods very attractive, since that is what we ask him to do. It follows that we cannot rest on the policy of *caveat emptor*, for this means only that we shall be given what we want, not necessarily what we need. It is this ability of the food manufacturer to separate our wants from our needs which must lead in due course to some legislation concerning the nutritional value of our foods. It will have to be more subtle than simply ensuring that our foods shall be processed in such a way as to conserve its nutrients as well as possible. It will have to take into account the fact that the existence of highly palatable new foods not only leads us to eat these foods, but tends to push other and perhaps more desirable foods out of our diets. Unless we devise legislation which prevents this sort of distortion of our diet, we shall increasingly run the risk of the malnutrition of affluence. There is already evidence that this ability of the food manufacturer to separate palatability from nutritional value contributes not only to the large number of people who are overweight, but also to diseases such as diabetes and coronary thrombosis.

On the other hand, the activities of the food manufacturer will be vastly increased in the direction of food preservation. Improvement in economic status, dependent upon increasing wealth, improvement in agricultural and processing techniques, and simple methods of birth control may enable a much greater proportion of mankind to share the increased food supplies. The present situation whereby only a small proportion of the world's peoples, in the wealthier countries, can have a wide range of foods at any time of the year, and from virtually any part of the world, will spread to most countries. There will also be fewer regional differences in the sorts of foods which people eat, as well as a decrease in difference in quantity.

One consequence of the tremendous advances in agricultural methods and food technology, which have contributed so much to improving our food supplies, is that our foods have become more uniform. Sometimes, they have also decreased in flavour, as have for example broiler chickens. With rising wages, the cost of producing 'old-fashioned' foods, such as free-range poultry, will rise. At first, this will no doubt mean that the cost of such foods will be prohibitive for almost everyone. By 1984, however, when our real incomes are likely to have increased greatly, there will be a sizeable proportion of the population in the affluent countries who can afford to indulge their preference for the much costlier foods produced for taste rather than for cheapness.

But, as we have seen, the increase of food availability will not automatically ensure good nutrition. By 1984, it is probable that we shall have enough information about the factors which determine food choice to ensure that we know how to bridge the gap between wide food availability and appropriate consumption.

In the presently impoverished countries of the world, we shall have to solve two dietary problems: how to persuade people to eat what is good for them, and how to prevent them from eating what is bad for them. In other words, the first problem is to persuade people accustomed to eating a narrow range of nutritionally poor foods to widen their choice so as to include the nutritionally more desirable foods, especially those rich in protein. We will need, for this purpose, information about what determines food habits and how people can be influenced to eat unaccustomed food – information which, at present, we have hardly begun to seek.

The second problem is to prevent the malnutrition of poverty from slipping directly into the malnutrition of affluence. As I have indicated, the latter will probably require some form of legislation, since it is difficult to see how any form of persuasion can overcome our inbred seeking after palatability in our food.

Fuel and Power

WORLD ENERGY PROSPECTS

by Sir Harold Hartley, F.R.S.

Central Electricity Generating Board, London

The policies of every nation, developed or emergent, are directed today towards economic growth. This is dependent on the availability of energy, the life-blood of industry and the vital factor in domestic comfort. So energy must play an important part in any economic forecast for 1984. The role of energy in a nation's well-being is shown graphically in Figure 1, in which the average

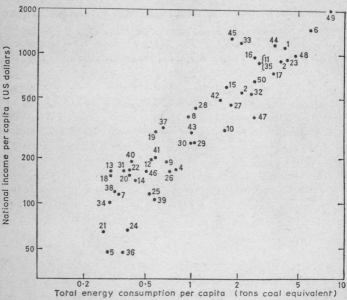

FIG. 1
The emergent countries are at the bottom left and the underdeveloped at the top right.

income *per capita* of fifty countries is plotted against their consumption of energy *per capita*. The coordination between the two is partly causal and partly due to effect. Abundant energy is needed for prosperity and this in turn raises the standard of living and the consumption of energy. Other factors such as climate come in to complicate the picture and no accurate statistics are available for the consumption of non-commercial sources of energy (wood, vegetable waste, and dung) which still play an important part in the more backward countries. However, the overall relationship between energy and well-being is abundantly clear.

How much energy is this world likely to consume in 1984? It will depend on the average consumption *per capita* and the growth of population. If the present trend continues, the average consumption of commercial energy *per capita* should be about 2·25 tons (metric throughout) of coal equivalent, and with a pro-jected world population of 4,500 millions the global energy con-sumption would be 10,000 million tons of coal equivalent, neglecting the non-commercial sources which are of declining significance. Global consumption in 1961 was 4,600 million tons of coal equivalent, taking into account the amount of coal saved by hydro-electricity.

The assessment of the proportions in which the amount of energy will be provided for the various primary sources is not so easy, as it has to take into account the trend of consumption shown in Table 1, relative price trends, and the economic progress of nuclear power and possibly of magneto-hydrodynamic (MHD) generation.

Table 1

Percentage world consumption of primary sources of energy

	Solid fuels	Liquid fuels	Natural gas	Hydro
1929	76·0	14·1	4·3	5·6
1937	70·0	17·0	6·0	7·0
1950	58·5	23·8	10·2	7·5
1961	47·3	30·3	14·6	7·8

Note: In this table and elsewhere in this article, hydro-electric power is given credit for the amount of coal equivalent it saves at the present average efficiency of steam generating stations.

The major change in the energy pattern in this century has been the increasing consumer demand, both in industry and in the home, for energy that has been upgraded into a more sophisticated form such as electricity, tailored liquid fuels, gas, and smokeless fuels, easy to distribute, handle, and use. In 1900 probably 90 per cent of the energy was consumed in the raw state as coal or wood, etc.; by 1929 that had fallen to 50 per cent; while by 1961 about 85 per cent was upgraded. Today about a quarter of the input of primary energy is consumed as electricity, the electric motor having displaced the steam engine in industry and an infinity of uses having been found for electricity as the most sophisticated form of energy. The refining of oil has provided the liquid fuels that are the basis of modern transport in nearly all its forms, and they have many other uses. Most of the natural gas, with its rapidly growing demand, has to be purified from sulphur before use.

The global forecast for 1984 has also to take into account the different trends in consumption of the three main consumer

Table 2

	Percentage of world population 1961	Percentage of world energy consumption	Per capita Energy consumption (tons, coal-equivalent)	Average annual percentage increase of per capita consumption 1951–61
N. America	6·5	37	7·8	0·44
W. Europe	9·5	31	2·6	2·4
Communist	33·0	20	1·25	10·4

groups of countries with the populations, consumptions, and growth rates. Table 2 shows that 49 per cent of the world's population consumes 88 per cent of the energy. No doubt the proximity of energy resources in these countries contributes to this state of affairs. Table 2 also shows the disparities between the *per capita* consumption in these groups of countries and the much more rapid growth of consumption in countries with the lowest average consumption.

If the consumption of electricity continues to increase at 7 per cent compound it will rise to $10,000 \times 10^9$ kWh in 1984. Supposing that 10 per cent is generated in nuclear stations in that year their contributions would be represented by about 400×10^6 tons coal equivalent. A significant contribution from MHD by 1984 is problematical.

Taking all these factors into consideration, the changes in the consumption of primary energy from 1961 to 1984 may look something like Figure 2. These estimates will serve at any rate as a basis for discussion, and forecasts will undoubtedly differ. By the 1980s we shall know which is right; with the rapid pace of technological development some quite unexpected changes may occur. The estimate for solid fuels takes into account the rapid rise in consumption in the Communist countries, which now consume 50 per cent of the world production of solid fuel with an

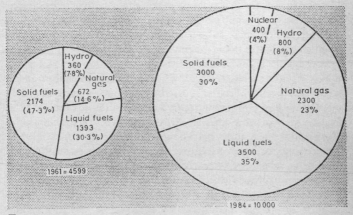

FIG. 2

World energy consumption in 1961 and 1984 (in million tons of coal equivalent).

annual increase of over 12 per cent since 1951. A large increase in the consumption of coal in North America is also forecast during the next twenty years.

These global figures, and the adequacy of world reserves to meet them, conceal the energy problems of individual countries. The pattern of energy consumption depends partly on the availability of indigenuos energy sources. Among the advanced countries, the U.S.S.R. is exceptional in being a net exporter of energy; Britain, Europe, and Japan are particularly dependent on imports of oil, and even the U.S.A. is a net importer. Moreover, the sources of energy are very unequally distributed between nations, as Table 3 shows.

Table 3

Location of 90 per cent of proved and estimated resources

Coal	U.S.A., U.S.S.R., and China
Oil	U.S.A., U.S.S.R., and Middle East
Natural gas	N. America, Middle East, U.S.S.R., N. Africa, Netherlands

Comprehensive estimates of water-power potentials are lacking; they appear to be more equally distributed, though here again the U.S.S.R. and U.S.A. have the major resources. The advanced countries are able to make good their deficiencies by imports for which they can afford to pay, but even there the flow is distorted by duties, quotas, and taxation.

Much thought is being given today to the problem of the emergent countries and to technical aid. How do they fare as regards energy ? Figure 1 shows the low level of their consumption *per capita*, and even where the gross consumption is increasing their rapid growth of population tends to nullify this advantage. With the exception of a few countries with large oil resources, notably in the Middle East and Africa, these developing countries lack indigenous resources of energy adequate to their population and their area, as energy is costly to transport over long distances except by tankers or by oil or natural-gas pipelines. By and large, energy presents no insuperable problems for the further development of the advanced countries by 1984; but it may be a serious handicap to the development of the less advanced countries, on whose progress in the future so much depends. The transport of energy in the form of nuclear fuel is the cheapest of all methods, so nuclear stations may in time provide for part of the needs of countries with inadequate indigenous energy resources.

A considerable effort has been directed to the development of the so-called 'new' sources of energy for use by the emergent countries – geothermal heat, wind power, and solar radiation. Geothermal heat is available in only a few localities; wind power is intermittent and storage of energy is expensive, unless it is used to pump water into a tank for storage; solar radiation, on the other hand, has considerable possibilities for domestic use by means of simple appliances and will undoubtedly help by 1984. The emergent countries with their dense populations living in small towns and villages need energy badly for light, for village industries, for the irrigation of crops and drainage, and for the local processing of their harvest of sugar, cotton, and jute. Energy for transport is also essential for their development. The solution of their energy problems should therefore be one of the first objectives of technical aid if the gap between the developed and emergent countries is to be narrowed by 1984.

THE USES OF ENERGY

by Dr J. Guéron

Head of Research, Euratom, Brussels

Looking at energy consumption patterns over the last thirty years, and considering how they vary today between countries at different stages of development, we need no second sight to foresee the uses for most of the increasing energy with which the world will be supplied during the next twenty years. Domestic electricity and transport have been greatly expanding outlets. Less than ten years ago, visiting a Japanese power station, I reckoned that its average customer had a 100-watt installation, or less. In 1930 in France, most houses were wired for 500 watts; now they are commonly provided with 3 to 5 kW. And 10 to 20 kW are commonplace in American homes. This domestic use has disconcerting variations, such as the evening TV peak (which may disappear in ten to twenty years with transistor sets) and the summer load increase from air-conditioning. Let us remember, too, that over 80 per cent of the installed power in the western world lies in car and truck engines (with a very low average load factor).

Industrial products, old and new, become more sophisticated and, despite improvements in production methods, require more energy per unit weight, or unit building capacity. From the usual figure of 1 kWh per kg we go up to 10 or 20, not to speak of the 100,000 to 500,000 which the separation of isotopes may require.

As for the developing countries, if they can be spared complete chaos in the close race between equipment and population, they will, in their applications of energy, follow the path which the western countries and the Soviet Union have taken in succession over the last century.

In this classical expansion, the main questions may be – apart from natural resources, which seem secure over twenty years at least – those of energy transport, of the ratio of peak load to base load, and of price.

Movement of oil, gas, and coal by pipeline will increase. Electricity transport may remain a problem because of the low consumption density in the developing world, and because of the high concentration of generating capacity in industrial countries (there has been a tenfold increase in the unit capacity of power stations in twenty years). Reduction of the peak-to-base ratio implies time-table rearrangements so upsetting for traditional social and family life that it is unlikely to be achieved extensively.

Provision of cheap power will be so vital in the developing countries that some system of state subsidy seems unavoidable. However, economic regulation of individual branches of industry – including power – seems desirable under all social and political systems, so that subsidies – and their counterpart, rationing – should be only temporary expedients.

In the industrialized world, we need a marked reduction in the cost of energy for certain very large-scale developments, probably in civil engineering, de-salting of brackish or sea water, mining and processing of low-grade ores, which have to be achieved in the next twenty to fifty years. However, no breakthrough towards low energy price seemed possible up to a few years ago. Recent developments of nuclear energy now, *perhaps*, seem able to achieve one.

This leads one to emphasize – and wonder at – the fact that the huge energy consumption of the last fifty years resulted from the dissemination of techniques established in principle long before. Of course, enormous ingenuity has gone into development, improvement of materials, design, economic planning. Nevertheless, fire, steam, running water, and rotating mechanical and electrical machinery still dominate the scene. This, indeed, has not been changed by the nuclear 'fire', now on the verge of extensive use after nearly twenty years of frustrated development, though it has stimulated the improvement of conventional systems by the fear of competition and by the trend towards very big generating units.

The dream of very cheap power, then, is still elusive. What of the next twenty years?

Solar energy is only indirectly used, through the natural water cycle, and in the indirect cycles of agriculture (one-year cycle for most crops, 40-year cycle in forests). At the same time we deplete the products of the million-year (or so) cycles of fossil fuels, without the least knowledge of their present phase.

The best efficiency of the agricultural cycle is below 10 per cent. Some improvement is possible, but a great general increase would imply concentration on particular crops with deep changes in food habits, and strong social resistance. However, a much greater use of the biological products of the sea could increase, if not the efficiency, at least the amount of the indirect use of solar energy.

Direct conversion to electricity can now be done with better than 10 per cent efficiency, which may well increase in coming years. However, the capital cost is high and the power density low (1 kW per sq. m – 5 to 10 sq. km at best for a mere 10 MW output). Weather and the unavoidable nights make it unthinkable to use solar electricity on a large scale, while the old problem of cheap electricity storage remains intractable. But, while massive production of solar electricity looks very remote – if not hopeless – one must not forget that, in small amounts, it has already, and will have, important uses. It is quite likely that, by 1984, the world communications system will be based on satellites' solar cells. This is a prime example of the *qualitative* importance of very small fractions of the total power supply.

Solar heat, however, seems to have a future, especially in the developing countries of the tropics. Mass production of suitable implements (solar cookers, boilers, and water-distillation units), together with a minimum of general education, could substantially improve the lot of up to 1,000 million human beings if technical and political action is steadily sustained.

But I do not believe, for advanced areas, in houses heated by solar energy, or powered by wind generators. Even if mass production could reduce costs and keep maintenance within reason, we are pampered people and would not stand the uncertain effects of the weather. We would retain parallel conventional equipment, aggravating in this way the load-factor problem. Here again, only a cheap, compact accumulator could change the picture. However, even if discovered now, the full impact of such a device would only begin to be felt after twenty years.

Direct – that is, non-mechanical – conversion of heat to electricity, especially by magneto-hydrodynamic processes, looks more hopeful, if the proper refractory materials can be developed. It would give great scope for using the high temperatures which, *in principle*, can be easily derived from nuclear fission or, perhaps, fusion.

We thus foresee, in 1984, an increased energy production and consumption on lines roughly similar to those of today. But what matters most are the qualitative developments which may occur in these twenty years and become of industrial and economic significance by the end of the century. Let us take the following examples from nuclear energy.

(1) Nuclear fusion may well have been demonstrated in prototypes by 1984. We can almost certainly ignore the possibility of any general use of nuclear fusion in twenty years, but, of course, the long-term economic importance of unlimited power from sea water can hardly be exaggerated.

(2) Very big nuclear vessels (ships or submarines) could become economic in the years ahead. But they could not be extensively used without a radical reconstruction of harbours and of their supporting continental transport system – which the coming megalopolis may independently provide.

(3) Water conservation and management assume increasing importance. Huge power- and heat-producing nuclear plants might provide a partial solution to the problem of converting salt water to fresh water. This is now hotly argued. If not discarded in the next few years, after thorough assessment, such a scheme (which will also test the possibility of producing very cheap nuclear electricity) will need a demonstration stage of some ten years for building and operating experience. If successful, it could be ripe for industrial expansion by 1980.

(4) Other aspects of the water problem (including hydroelectric development), some mining operations, and other activities will require extensive civil engineering works. These are now carried out by mechanical means vastly more efficient than, but basically derived from, the pick and shovel. Armies of men

spend years in completing them. Explosives are used, but in a very limited way because of price, lack of experience in using them for industrial purposes in huge amounts, and low energy density. The latter is similar to current fuel combustion (say 10 kWh of heat per kg). Nuclear explosives have an energy density at least one million times greater. It is now very likely that underground nuclear explosions can be managed so as to produce surface excavation with nearly complete containment of undesirable radio-activity. The road seems thus open to 'geographical engineering' which, on a grand scale, could afford increased access to conventional fuel and ore reserves, and climate modification, at least locally. A first experiment (creation of a harbour in Alaska) was cancelled because the radiation hazards were not fully mastered. But if the political implications of test explosions can be overcome, development work can be expected to continue, and demonstration projects should have been carried out before 1984.

In nuclear power production some 5 per cent of the energy appears as penetrating gamma-rays ('prompt', or 'delayed' in fission products). These now begin to be used in chemical, bio-chemical, and biological work (sterilization, food preservation, production of mutations, radiochemical polymerization). Here again, one can foresee, with enough development, special uses of a particular form of energy which may create new products and deeply transform existing industries. It is clear that where food preservation is concerned the economic consequences are enormous. Already we expect that potato sprouting in storage can be eliminated.

All these possibilities could and should be elaborated and discussed in more detail, and others considered. But it remains clear that, in 1984, the bulk of power production and consumption will be very traditional, with a number of radical explorations in many directions. By the end of the century the picture might well be significantly different.

NEW SOURCES OF ELECTRICITY

by Dr Ian Fells

Reader in Fuel Science, University of Newcastle-upon-Tyne

The conversion of energy from one form into another has been a major preoccupation of man throughout his existence. The generation of heat by fire, the conversion of the potential energy of a stretched bow string into the deadly kinetic energy of the arrow, the production of explosions of ever increasing magnitude, are all energy-conversion processes.

Electricity is probably the most generally useful intermediate form of energy. It can be quickly and easily converted into heat, light, kinetic energy, communication waves, and so on, and it can be stored ready for use. The convenience of electrical energy is reflected in the price of £5 a kilowatt-hour we are prepared to pay for electrical energy stored in a dry battery.

The doubling of electricity requirements each decade means that in 1984 at least three quarters of the electricity required will be generated by plant not yet constructed. The development of new, more efficient methods of generating electricity are clearly worthwhile.

In the field of large-scale generation the efficiency of conversion has gradually climbed to 37 per cent, mainly as a result of building larger units (500 MW) with increased steam temperatures. This trend will continue but it is unlikely that units of larger than 750 MW will be built, as serious problems of availability then arise.

Conversion efficiencies should rise to between 45 and 48 per cent by 1984. The whole field of large-scale electricity generation may well be changed if 'magneto-hydrodynamic' methods of power generation are developed successfully. Considerable research effort is being put into MHD generation on both sides of the Atlantic. A 40-megawatt fossil fuel unit is already constructed and undergoing development in the United States, and a similar unit is proposed by the Central Electricity Generating Board. These systems are relatively unsophisticated but point the way to future developments. Within the next twenty years a second MHD generation system, now at the research stage and based on 'non-equilibrium' processes, might well have reduced the operating temperatures to levels that can be tolerated by engineering materials.

The power station of 1984, whether it be a nuclear or fossil fuel station, might consist of an MHD 'topping' generator exhausting either into a conventional steam-driven generating set giving an overall efficiency of between 60 and 65 per cent, or feeding a combined thermionic-thermoelectric system giving a rather better overall efficiency of conversion.

This development might well influence the price 'break-even' date for nuclear generated electricity. If MHD topping proves easier with fossil fuels than with nuclear heat sources a reappraisal of power-station building programmes will be needed.

In any event the advent of MHD generation will radically alter the present design of generating sets and could well stimulate a new look in the design of conventional water tube boilers. The separation of the combustion and heat-transfer processes, or the systems utilizing the high heat-transfer rates possible with oscillating combustion systems and sub-cooled boiling processes could lead to conventional fossil-fuel stations with high output but small physical dimensions.

Another far-reaching development lies in the possibility of on-site, silent, and efficient electricity generation by fuel cells. Cells are already available which can operate on fuels as varied as hydrogen, methane, light hydrocarbons, methanol, hydrazine, and, in certain circumstances, such intractable materials as tar or even brandy can be used. Efficiencies of energy conversion of 60 per cent are quite realistic and during the next decade the present problems of long-term reliability and low-temperature operation on the less reactive fuels will most probably be solved. The advantages of fuel cells are silent operation, high conversion efficiency, ability to burn a variety of fuels efficiently, and simplicity of scale-up by the assembly of larger banks of cells. The main disadvantage lies in the low-voltage d.c. output, but solid state converters make conversion to alternating current cheap and easy.

The recent announcement of light, high-speed, d.c. electric motors already points the way to revolutionary changes in methods of traction. The result of fuel-cell development in the next twenty years could lead to an entirely new look in car design with a fuel cell driving an electric motor built into the hub of each wheel. That would eliminate the transmission system as we know it, and would mean maximum torque at minimum engine speed, a pollution-free exhaust, no fuel consumption when stationary in traffic jams, and complete freedom for the car designer to fit the car round the occupants rather than the engine. In the case of rail traction the chief advantage of a fuel-cell power unit, apart from increased conversion efficiency, is the absence of power supply lines and consequently greatly increased flexibility.

Fuel cells are particularly suited to replace conventional diesel- and petrol-driven generators in the 10 kW range. Silence and the absence of moving parts taken in conjunction with a conversion efficiency of 60 rather than 10 per cent make fuel cells particularly attractive for providing an electricity supply in yachts, house-boats, remote farms, and caravans. By 1984 the noise problems arising from outboard motors of small boats may well have been solved by replacing the offending engines by electric motors. The military applications are obvious. Plans for a fuel-cell-powered submarine are already well developed.

Domestic electricity supplies in 1984 could well be radically altered by installing a fuel-cell generator in each house and small factory, running off piped hydrocarbon gases. Distribution of gas is much cheaper than distribution of electricity. In Britain, the new oil gasification processes produce a gas which is suitable for use in a fuel cell, and the growing supply of natural gas is another factor which may well encourage the introduction of domestic fuel cells by 1984. Such a system would have the added advantage that the hydrocarbon fuel cell would probably operate in the 200–400° C. range and an integral central-heating system could be built into each generator, thus making effective use of the heat given out during the electricity generation process.

The development of cells operating on natural gas will put an end to the burning to waste of natural gas in the arid, oil-producing areas of the world. The gas will be used in large units to generate electricity, to operate irrigation pumps, and to provide local electricity supplies. Not only fuel cells will be used but also new thermionic and thermoelectric generators which, although heat engines, and unlikely to achieve conversion efficiencies of better than 15 to 20 per cent, have the advantage of no moving parts and consequently simple maintenance. In 1984 the underdeveloped countries, particularly in arid, hot areas of the world, may well be using local fuel-cell electricity supplies, a rugged, simple, fuel-cell-powered electric tractor, and irrigation schemes running off thermionic and thermoelectric generators converting solar heat into electricity.

Thermionic and thermoelectric converters, in addition to their role in underdeveloped areas and their obvious applications in spacecraft will almost certainly contribute towards reducing the appalling waste of heat which occurs in large industrial plant. The average steelworks, for example, could generate enough electricity from the heat lost from hot metal to operate all the auxiliary pumps, fans, lighting, and so on in the works.

Methods of electricity storage will certainly change during the next twenty years. In small-scale applications a miniaturized fuel cell operating from a cartridge of gaseous fuel rather like the one used in a cigarette lighter will provide low voltage d.c. for lighting, portable radios, etc. On a large scale, the storing of excess electricity in chemical form (hydrogen and oxygen are examples but there are many other possibilities) which can be quickly regenerated in a fuel cell will enable peak loads and unexpected demands to be met without the need to install large power stations which will only be used intermittently. The present method of storage by water-pumping is only applicable in special (and usually remote) geographical locations.

There are a variety of special applications of the new methods of generation. One of the more striking ideas is the biochemical fuel cell which converts energy available in biochemical systems into electricity. The currents available are usually small, but a small fuel cell immersed in the appropriate body fluids could generate enough power to operate a heart 'pacemaker' in a patient.

The new methods of generating electricity outlined here are not new. Grove built a fuel cell in 1842 and Faraday carried out MHD experiments before 1840. They are now probabilities rather than possibilities because the advent of new materials and a desire to make better use of our dwindling resources have stimulated the interest of applied scientists. The combined forces of economic necessity and technological ingenuity will undoubtedly lead within two decades to more convenient and efficient generation of electricity and to some, at least, of the innovations suggested here.

Materials and Manufacture

DESIGNING THE MATERIALS WE NEED

by Professor R. A. Smith, F.R.S.

Center for Materials Science and Engineering, Massachusetts Institute of Technology

Materials science is passing through a marked transitional period at present so that prediction is a chancy business. However, many trends are discernible and some fruits of a changed attitude to the means of developing new materials have already been gathered. In the past, such development has been largely empirical and it is amazing how much success has been achieved by this means. For example, steels used in the Middle Ages by swordmakers in Japan, Damascus, and Spain have not been bettered as regards tensile strength (except in the form of cold-drawn wire). The development of these steels took a very long time with much trial and error and in this modern industrial age the time and effort are just not available. The transition which is taking place is from empirical methods to the controlled construction of man-made materials and has come about largely through the great advances which have taken place in solid-state physics. There are still many basic problems to be solved and the need for fundamental research is greater than ever.

Steel will still be with us as a widely used material in 1984 but will have been improved enormously, since we now understand many of the functions of deliberately added impurities. It is so important as a material that it is the subject of a separate contribution. Steel will not, however, meet all our needs in 1984 for a high-tensile ductile material; it loses much of its strength at high temperatures. For the leading edges of supersonic aircraft it would be inadequate, and for spacecraft, where kinetic heating on re-entry into the atmosphere will raise the temperature to well over $1,400^\circ$ C., the approximate melting point of most steels, it would be useless. Here it is likely to be superseded by alloys of the refractory metals such as zirconium, niobium, molybdenum, or tungsten. Metals in use in 1984 may well be composite, consisting of minute globules of metals with lower melting points embedded in the refractory metals. Composite materials of this kind have shown promise of giving the ductility needed for forming them into the required shapes, are much less brittle, and retain a fair measure of these properties as well as their strength at high temperatures.

An entirely different approach to this problem comes through the development of new ceramic materials. These have many of the heat-resistant properties required but lack the strength and ductility of metals. Until recently the development of ceramics has certainly been an art rather than a science, but this phase is passing. Basic studies of the structure of ceramics have shown that defects on an atomic scale are largely the cause of the failure of ceramics to stand up to the strength requirements. Control of these defects should lead to greatly improved materials of this kind.

An important class of composite materials consists of aggregates of different substances. Concrete is a rather crude example. More subtle examples are in the form of fibrous materials. It is found that many materials, made in the form of thin filaments, can be very free from defects and exceptionally strong. These fibres can be embedded in a matrix and may form the basis of new materials. Flexibility and freedom from fatigue come about from the fact that the thin fibres may be bent very easily and frequently without breaking. In this class of composite materials also come 'solid foams'. These have a high strength-to-weight ratio and could be glazed to give a protective finish. Such materials made from high-melting-point oxides have been suggested for the leading edges of wings of supersonic aircraft but will have a multitude of other uses, including that of providing heat insulation at high temperatures.

Although the material requirements of aviation and space flight have given rise to some of the most difficult problems and have tended to have much of the limelight, these represent only a very small fraction of the requirements for the technological advances twenty years from now. By then we shall see great changes in building construction which will require lighter, tougher, and more elegant materials than we have now. For all but special buildings where expense is no object and traditional design is desirable, the use of stone and brick will largely have disappeared by 1984, and happily we shall have passed out of the grey concrete age.

The new materials will mainly be derived from high polymers and, in addition to strength and beauty, they will provide thermal and sound insulation and ease of working. These will be a consequence of the present basic studies of the processes and of the control of polymerization (the making of big molecules out of little ones). This class of materials will also give us a much better type of paint for both decorative and protective purposes. The emulsion paints now in use are only a beginning of a movement towards this type of material based on controlled polymerization. The continuing need of new fabrics for dress and interior decoration should also be met by new types of fibres based on polymers. Glass is an excellent material for transparent construction and is unlikely to be superseded. It is likely that much less brittle forms will be developed.

The need for fuels for space travel and for other requirements where bulk is a severe disadvantage will undoubtedly lead to the development of new solid fuels which are much more concentrated than those currently in use. This is a very large subject which we cannot discuss in this brief article. The development of an entirely new type of material is, however, of very great interest, and should be mentioned. This type of material is the converse of a fuel. A fuel consists of material which when reacted chemically, usually with oxygen, produces a strongly exothermic reaction, the heat of which is used to produce motive power or just heat. The new material is one which produces a strongly endothermic reaction and by this means can absorb heat. A rather crude example of this type of material is a plastic which absorbs heat when charred. Materials of this kind will be developed to absorb the intense heat generated on the nose-cones of spacecraft re-entering the atmosphere, and may have a number of other uses.

In addition to constructional materials many new materials for special technological purposes will be in use in 1984, for example, in electronic equipment, the use of which will be even more widespread than at present. These new materials will be like either the germanium used in transistors, first made ultra-pure and then modified with minute controlled amounts of impurity, or man-made materials like indium antimonide. Special new optical materials, of which the existing laser materials are just a crude beginning, will have revolutionized optical systems, and new superconducting alloys will enable very high magnetic fields to be generated without dissipation of large quantities of electrical power.

One very important field in which great advances may be expected in the next twenty years is that of biological materials. Some of these materials, originally studied in a form obtained from living organisms, can now be man-made – many more will be made, with controlled variations, in the next twenty years. The potential consequences of this in medicine are tremendous either for evil or for good, depending on man's moral attitude to their use. This is far too big a subject for this article but also far too important not to be mentioned.

The new materials of 1984 will largely be the ones that man needs most urgently. The days of 'cut and try' are nearly over and materials science is moving into an age of control. Man should be able to design the materials he needs, and the next twenty years will see great steps in this direction. It will not be achieved, how-ever, without extensive research in physics. Many of the basic facts about how solids hang together, what are the factors that weaken them, that give them ductility, or make them brittle and so on are gradually being brought to light. An important develop-ment of this age is the cooperation of staff from different academic disciplines, such as physics, chemistry, and metallurgy, in so-called 'interdisciplinary laboratories' to make a determined attack on some of the basic problems of materials science. On the biological side we are just beginning to see the cooperation of biologists, chemists, and physicists in a similar attack on biological materials. By 1984 we should be picking some of the fruits.

STRONGER STEEL FOR WIDER PURPOSES

by W. E. Duckworth
British Iron and Steel Research Association, London

No material in sight can rival steel in its combination of strength and low cost. As a result, 93 per cent of the metal used in the world is steel or other ferrous-based material, and there is no reason to expect that this proportion will have changed significantly by 1984.

Steel will then be stronger and tougher as well as being cleaner and more consistent. The most common structural steels, those used in bridges and in the skeletons for buildings, may have a yield strength of around 45 tons/sq. in. as against the current value for mild steel of 15 tons/sq. in. and the present 'high-tensile steels' of the 18–22 tons/sq. in. Despite the higher yield strengths these steels will be more readily weldable than the current high-tensile steels and will be much tougher and able to withstand much lower temperatures before becoming liable to 'brittle fracture'.

Stainless steel will also be very much stronger than it is at present, both in sheet form suitable for supersonic aircraft and in thick plate used for chemical plant and other purposes.

Low alloy steel used in many applications in motor cars and aircraft, and which currently has a tensile strength of around 70–100 tons/sq. in. will have strengths around 150 tons/sq. in. but be just as tough as the present materials.

Extremely high-strength steels, having strengths of around 200 tons/sq. in., may be common, and special welding techniques will have been developed so that these steels can be used in applications not yet envisaged. All the other common components of steel – wires, bolts, reinforcing rods, etc. – will have strengths about 50 per cent greater than those in common use today. They will enable much lighter and more elegant structures to be built, and many advanced designs using high-strength steels in combination with concrete should be in use.

The problems of machining very high-strength steels will have been overcome, either by the use of greatly improved tool steels and machining techniques, or by the use of lasers or chemical machining methods, and engineers will be thoroughly accustomed to handling materials which are at present thought to be unmanageable. The machining problems will also be reduced by the greater use of extrusion to produce components to near-finished size. Powder metallurgical techniques will also help.

There will be some improvement in the corrosion resistance of steel and though this is not likely to be very marked, the problem of corrosion will continue to decrease in importance as the result of improved coatings and design methods. A substantial change will also have taken place in the form in which steel is sold. Very little uncoated sheet steel or steel sections will be sold. It will all have been spray-painted, aluminized, or perhaps temporarily coated to protect it before and during shipment from the steelworks, and all that the fabricator will have to do is to erect the steel in position and give it a final coat or two of paint. Much steel will, however, be finish-coated with stainless steel, non-ferrous metals, or plastics in the works.

In 1984 it is likely that the blast furnace will still be the main method of winning iron from its ore. Furnaces might even be smaller than the 30–32 ft diameter of today but outputs will be 5,000 to 6,000 tons per day. Tonnage oxygen and injected fuels, together with pre-reduction of ore, will make these high outputs possible. A significant proportion of iron may be produced by direct reduction processes, particularly in countries where advantageous combinations of ore and oil or gas occur. It is possible that countries with suitable ore deposits will be making iron for shipment elsewhere, instead of shipping ore, as at present. The overall efficiency of the iron-making process will have increased through better use of metallurgical slags, and advanced slag-based building materials will be finding profitable applications.

From the blast furnace on, however, steelmaking processes will be more 'continuous' than at present. The oxygen converter will probably still be the main process used for the larger quantities of steel, but advancement of automatic weighing and conveying techniques will be making outputs of about 400 tons per hour very common. Several completely continuous processes of steelmaking will be in operation, either using electromagnetic pumping systems to convey the molten steel or refining it in fine droplet form in passage from one ladle to another. After the initial refining to remove carbon, silicon, sulphur, and phosphorus from the iron, the final refining operations will probably take place in vacuum and the casting of the ingots, even for large quantities of steel, may also be carried out under vacuum. In this way cleaner and more consistent steels will be produced and it is highly probable that the bulk engineering steels will be produced to a standard of quality at present only achieved by the special alloy steels. Special steels will be improved still further by processing in inert atmospheres made as a by-product of the large oxygen producing plants which will be in common use.

Much more instrumentation and automation will be used throughout the ironmaking and steelmaking processes. The raw materials being fed into the blast furnace and into the steel-making converters will be weighed and analysed continuously, and 'feed-forward' control will be used to anticipate the output and composition of the final product, which will be checked against the actual results and the information obtained used to improve the control. Continuous analysis of the steel and waste gases during processing will enable feed-back controls to be employed to increase reliability and reproducibility of operation.

Although the major steelworks of the world will still be using basically the same processes for conversion of molten steel into steel products as at present – producing ingots and then rolling or forging them to the final shape – a significant telescoping of processes will have begun to occur. Continuous casting will be one such technique; here the molten steel is cast into something approaching the final size required, the finishing operation being performed by a rolling mill of smaller power than required at present. Sheet, strip, rod, bar, and billets may also be made directly from continuously cast steel, and possibly up to 30 per cent of the final steel products will be made by such processes.

Another technique which may be making a significant contribution by 1984 will be the direct production of steel parts from powder. The molten steel will be atomized into fine droplets which will be solidified, collected, sieved and sorted, and then rolled, compressed or extruded into the shape required before being finally sintered. Extremely thin strip will probably be made this way, as may sheet and rod which have to preserve useful strength at a high temperature. It is possible that the stainless steel sheet required for the fuselages of supersonic aircraft will be made from stainless-steel powder by this process. There will be much more automation in the more conventional forging and rolling techniques and much more accurate finishing of parts to their final size will be practised. Some steelworks will be completely automated and the manufacturing processes and scheduling operations will all be controlled by computers.

The total world output of steel by 1984 will probably be in the region of 700 million tons a year, and the largest producers may be the Soviet Union, America, Japan, and India. Most of the developing countries will have small steelworks of their own capable of satisfying their simplest requirements for structural engineering materials. The more advanced steel-producing countries such as Britain, in addition to satisfying their own basic needs, will be placing special emphasis on the higher qualities of steel and on the more imaginative kind of steel-using product. There will have been an increase in the use of steel for many novel purposes and combinations of steel with other materials, in addition to those already mentioned, will be common.

WORKING WITH NEW MATERIALS

by Sir Denning Pearson
Rolls-Royce Ltd, Derby

In considering what general progress will have been made in materials by 1984 and what will be available to engineers by this date, it must be remembered that, according to past experience, a time cycle of the order of ten to twenty years is normally required between the first inception of a new material and its eventual commercial applications. This being so, it seems unlikely that any dramatic improvements in this general field, on which we have not already seen some indications, will be available by 1984.

Over the next twenty years we can expect a steady development of knowledge and technology which will produce improved materials for particular purposes and their applications will be governed by the overall economics. In parallel with this there will be the development of relatively new concepts which have appeared during the last decade – and also completely new concepts of materials, with which I shall deal later.

One of the more difficult metallurgical problems is that of the materials for gas turbine applications, particularly for the still higher operating temperatures which will be demanded in the future. Metals such as chromium, molybdenum, niobium, tantalum, and tungsten will find specialized applications in this field, although so far these materials have not been used in highly stressed engineering components. Over a period of fifteen years great attention has been focused on molybdenum and more recently on niobium. Unfortunately, molybdenum has limited ductility and catastrophic oxidation, due to the volatility of the oxide. In spite of great efforts these serious limitations have not been satisfactorily overcome. Niobium exhibits more promise and will probably be in use by 1984. It has the advantages over molybdenum of being lighter and ductile over a greater range of temperatures, and although there is still a high-temperature oxidation problem, there is hope that it can be overcome by alloying or by protective coating.

It is visualized that chromium will be used for certain turbine-blade applications because it has sufficient strength, is lighter and there are distinct signs that its known disadvantages of nitrogen absorption and low temperature brittleness will yield to metallurgical research. Tantalum and tungsten, although under consideration at the moment, are improbable contenders in the aircraft turbine engine, as not only do they have the disadvantages of molybdenum, niobium, and chromium, but they are heavier.

At lower temperatures, the use of beryllium in stressed structural materials is a comparatively recent innovation. This material, with an elastic modulus approximately 50 per cent greater than that of steel and with a density of only 5 per cent above magnesium, has great potential, if its disabilities with regard to ductility can be overcome. This appears to be a basic problem of the beryllium crystal, and its solution may prove to be difficult.

Developments in the control of impurities in metals by vacuum techniques will contribute as much to the development of engineering materials as will physical metallurgy.

An example of the new concepts of materials is that in which weaker materials are strengthened or reinforced by either particles or filaments. The first idea, known as dispersion hardening, has met with limited success in high-temperature materials and spectacular developments are not envisaged. The second idea, filament strengthening, has proved more successful and has found, up to now, its main application in materials other than metals. Such materials are already in use for highly stressed components, and it is now possible to produce plastics reinforced by glass having a tensile strength of 90 tons/sq. in. Plastics are already known which can withstand temperatures of 450° C., and undoubtedly there will be available in the future improved strength filaments and a further extension of the upper limit of temperature of the matrix, and such materials will find increasing applications.

What of speculation on the possibilities of achieving radical improvements in materials? We have known for a long time that the theoretical strengths of solids, based on our understanding of interatomic forces, are in the region of a thousand tons per square inch while the strengths which are actually encountered in nature are in the region of tens of tons per square inch. Research work is now revealing how strengths more nearly approaching these very high theoretical values can be achieved and maintained, particularly with modern ceramic materials, oxides, borides, carbides, and nitrides which, in addition to having high strengths, can also have low densities, high stiffnesses, good corrosion resistance, and high temperature capabilities.

Such materials may be used in the form of reinforcing filaments, in conjunction with high temperature alloys – the latter then being relieved of the duty of load carrying and acting essentially as glues bonding together the ceramic filaments. Use as reinforcements will overcome the main shortcoming of these ceramics – their extreme brittleness – and the required toughness for engineering structures will be provided by the composite nature of the material.

In ways such as these we will be evolving towards the engineering equivalent of biological materials, with polyphase structures having specialized constituents to perform specialized functions. Since the technology of any age is founded upon the materials of the age, this new era of composite materials will have a profound effect on engineering in the future. To the designer, limited by the uniform nature of present-day materials, these concepts will give a new degree of freedom, and there will be opened up a field of micro-engineering design. Just as, in making an engine, we do not start with one large piece of uniform material and machine the whole engine out of it, but design each component in the most suitable material and then assemble them, so with composite materials the engineer will be able to design in detail the insides of components, giving non-uniform properties, such as greater strength in a preferred direction, or with differences in properties in various parts of the same components.

Turning now to the problem of manufacture, one may make the initial specific comment that, with the evolution of composite materials, there will develop manufacture by synthesis, in which components will be made by building them up from sub-component constituents. However, considering the more general aspects of manufacturing, two factors will have a significant influence on techniques twenty years hence. First, the continuing need for higher productive efficiency in the interests of both domestic and national economy, and, secondly, the characteristics of high-performance materials constantly under development.

It is inevitable that the skilled operator as he is recognized today will, in large measure, be replaced by programme-controlled machine tools and other equipment. Working hours will become progressively shorter, and the new skills will lie in the programming of manufacturing functions and the understanding and maintenance of highly sophisticated equipment.

The transfer of computer information direct from designer to tool manufacturer is already a practical possibility and the intermediate stages of component detailing and tool design will, in time, become insignificant items in the cost of prototype manufacture.

Automatic tool changing and presentation of the workpiece to the cutting tool through the medium of taped instructions will become the rule rather than the exception, and, while the machinist himself will fall into the category of 'minder' rather than operator and may well have two or more highly specialized units running simultaneously under his control, he will need to possess a higher standard of intelligence and technical competence than is customary today.

Factories already exist where automation is complete and, whilst currently the principle is applied only to highly repetitive work, the spread of automation will continue and countries which lack the initiative and enthusiasm to keep pace with this form of progress will suffer economically. However, it must never be overlooked that quantity without quality is in the long term a totally useless commodity. Therefore the ability to maintain set standards right from raw material to finished article must be an integral feature of any automated process.

Techniques of metal removal and manipulation will undergo

rapid changes as materials inevitably become more difficult to machine and the resistance to change of shape is increased by improvements in physical properties. It is already apparent that electro-chemical and other forms of 'chipless' machining will become essential tools in any modern workshop and that machining with the aid of gaseous mixtures, ultrasonics, and plasma arc may also become conventional tools of the future.

Materials which are difficult to handle in the solid state will encourage the automation of foundry techniques, just as the need for improved utilization of material is leading in the direction of high-energy forging to close limits and the use of very much higher forging pressures often in association with closed-die techniques. The rolling of gear teeth and serrations straight from the turned blank may be expected to supersede cutting and hobbing for all but the very highest performance transmission systems.

In the field of fabrication, we can look forward to more widespread use of electron-beam welding – almost certainly divorced from its vacuum chamber – and laser systems will develop in competition with other forms of welding. In the same way that hand control will be eliminated from machining operations, the configuration of fabrication structures will be influenced by the need for automatic control of welding processes in the interests of quality and productivity.

Also, the forming of high-strength sheet materials which do not lend themselves to manipulation by conventional press methods will encourage the development of electro-hydraulic, electro-magnetic and stress stretch/press techniques.

These thoughts are based on present trends, and do not take into account revolutionary inventions and changes or the influence of world political situations which may well arise during the next twenty years. It is, in fact, safer to predict progress in manufacturing techniques in those countries which afford a high degree of priority to technical education and research rather than in those which hang on grimly to established practice and traditional skill and craftsmanship.

HIGH-SPEED AUTOMATIC WORKSHOPS

by Pierre Bézier

Régie Nationale des Usines Renault, Billancourt, France

If one tries to see what industry will be like in twenty years' time, one should carefully distinguish the technically possible from the economically reasonable. Keeping this need in mind, we shall try to forecast the progress that manufacturing methods will have made by 1984.

The new high purity steels are very likely to be widely used. Their tensile strength will be above that of many alloys in use at the present time, and distortion resulting from heat treatment will be greatly reduced. In many cases, this will simplify or abolish some of the subsequent operations. By using induction hardening processes, components will be locally treated on the production line, thereby eliminating the gathering together of heat-treatment facilities into one shop and simplifying handling problems.

Aluminium will encroach increasingly on the domain of steel and particularly cast iron, and will not itself be seriously threatened by competition from magnesium. Diecasting techniques have greatly improved in the past few years, and there will be no surprise in obtaining aluminium parts weighing well over 200 lb. by this process. The accuracy obtained will probably not be sufficient to make machining unnecessary.

At present, all cast and forged parts are produced with an allowance for machining. Any techniques which can produce to closer limits, such as powder metallurgy, 'lost-wax' processes, and cold forging methods, are assured of considerable development. Lost-wax casting will remain rather slow and expensive, and it will be applied mainly to very complex parts. Cold or 'semi-hot' forging, being much faster, will be used in many cases for mass production of rough parts.

Synthetic materials will certainly figure more often in manufacture. They are easily and rapidly formed to such accurate dimensions that they seldom require any machining operation apart from 'barrel tumbling'. At present the curing time of resins limits the production rate, but chemists will certainly overcome this difficulty and, from then on, we shall often use plastics instead of metal.

Improvement in machine design is closely allied to the progress made in the cutting tools. First high-speed and then carbide tools necessitated increased machine speeds. This in its turn forced designers to build increased rigidity into machines to avoid vibrations which would have a detrimental effect on tool life.

Ceramic tools have found, up to now, only limited application. The importance of the part they will play depends on the possible improvement brought to their resistance to shocks. The machines will also have to be fast and rigid enough to exploit all the possibilities of such tools. In these conditions, the cutting speed which undoubtedly will be reached in steel or cast iron can be 1,000 ft per minute or more.

As cutting speeds increase, swarf removal becomes more and more difficult, especially where drilling and turning are concerned. Very likely, the increasing cutting speeds will cause chip breakage and, at the same time, a large quantity of swarf will have to be removed. Consequently, the machines' shape will have to be radically altered, and the Swiss 'G+F' lathe is a first example of such a change. Here the guiding arrangements are placed above the part to be machined, and the frame is wide open so as to let the chips fall through into troughs leading to a collecting station where they will be centrifuged, crushed, baled, and sent to the foundry.

There will still be a large difference between mass-production shops and general engineering shops. The first will be mainly equipped with special machines, whose general aspect will not show many changes from what we know today, except for speed and strength; but static switching devices will have replaced relays, and the controls will then be placed within the structure of the machine, clearing most of control cabinets away.

Loading of parts and storage of work in progress will be automatized, saving labour, giving a better output from the machines, and reducing 'downtimes' between operations. This tendency is already evident in some machining lines; it will spread to stamping and welding shops as well.

The aim of keeping downtimes to a minimum in mass-production shops working at the rate of several parts per minute will inevitably entail constant checking of tools and, sometimes, in case of wear or breakage, their automatic change. Manpower will be mainly employed in surveillance, checking, and maintenance, and will perform no manual handling of the parts.

Will there be a tendency to a drastic reduction of machining tolerances ? That is doubtful, as they are already down to 0·0004 inch. Reaching closer limits would mean constant temperature of shops, parts, standards, and, apart from very accurate tasks, there is no justification for such expensive arrangements.

It is no longer rare to see automatic machines carrying out assembly of products from components. This tendency will continue, but the products to be thus manufactured will have to be designed so as to simplify the task given to the machine.

General engineering problems are most diverse and less easy to solve. Regarding machining jobs, numerical control is bound to play an important part. It allows quick passage from one job to another without any compromise on accuracy, and the general output of such machines is far better than that of conventional plant. Numerical control also allows the use of highly skilled men on work preparation and lets semi-skilled labour operate the machines. This technique will then help solve such problems as shortage of skilled labour. Numerical control will take part in production of patterns, dies, or masters of intricate shape, when combined with spark erosion or electrochemical machining and more conventional machining methods.

For short runs 'high-energy' methods will play an important part in metal forming. We find electrical energy easier to handle and less dangerous than explosives, so that the latter will only be applied to build prototypes and for very small batch production; the electrical method, on the other hand, may be used for medium- and mass-production where conventional machines would need complex tooling.

The trend towards automation will become more and more intensive in the future. Already existing in mass-production shops, automation will spread to general engineering, in which numerical control will play a major part. Highly skilled workers, instead of operating machines, will be responsible for the process scheduling, and, in this, they will be helped by computers. Production-shop managers will have to ensure that work flow is steady, and divide it between machines, instead of checking whether these jobs are correctly performed by conventional means, since the instructions, being given automatically, are automatically followed. Work will be organized according to the possible load of machines, delay for each part, price of work in progress, and operator availability. The use of electronic computers will be compulsory because they can, in a very short time, view the whole problem and test any possible solution before choosing the best one.

We may suppose that, apart from special jobs where performances are more important than costs, the general aspect of the workshops will remain about the same. The observer will only notice that machines will be more powerful and will work faster; practically all handling will be automatic, labour will be scarcer; a few new techniques will appear.

But the major change will happen in management thinking: better knowledge of the properties of materials, more thorough study of process engineering, more scientific planning of production, whether to do with the curve a tool describes or the flow of parts handled through a shop. Management will have to approach these new techniques with an even more progressive mind.

The promise of the future is greater production, at a better price, using less labour. To realize it, leaders of industry will have to keep themselves thoroughly informed of all the possibilities new techniques can offer; but common sense and far-sightedness will dictate their choice.

Oceans

NEW AND RICHER MARINE HARVESTS FORECAST

by Professor Sir Alister Hardy, F.R.S.

University of Oxford

Will science and technology be bringing us more food from the sea in 1984 than we take from it today ? Yes, I believe so.

While the more novel ventures may come in the wide oceans, let us first consider their shallower margins which support the conventional fisheries of today. Except for shellfish culture, man at present, with his trawls and drift-nets, is still a hunter and a trapper in the sea. The question now being asked is 'Could we not use methods akin to farming ?' Actually the first steps in this direction are already being taken.

J. E. Shelbourne, of the Fisheries Laboratory of the British Ministry of Agriculture, Fisheries, and Food, has for several years been developing techniques for rearing young plaice in tanks from hatching to the stage when they settle on the sea-bed; he has carried them in thousands safely through what, in nature, is the most dangerous period of their lives, when they are the prey of countless enemies. By using antibiotics he has achieved 70 per cent success; and this year will see the completion of a plant at Port Erin in the Isle of Man to turn out a million fish a year. The plaice passes through these stages in the spring, and the sole in the autumn; so Mr Shelbourne plans to keep his plant in continual production by alternating the two. Before long he will be turning out not one, but ten, million fish a year, and by 1984 there may well be many such 'factories' spread along the coasts.

Such advances may bring overcrowding to the coastal waters, so stultifying growth as the young fish compete for the limited food available. If so, we shall have to resurrect a former plan. The late Professor Walter Garstang, early in the century, trawled up thousands of young plaice from the overcrowded coastal belt of Holland; he measured and tagged them, and then set half free at once, but carried the rest in tanks to the richer grounds of the Dogger Bank. When they were caught again and measured he found that the Bank fish had grown three, four, and five times as much as those left behind; he then proposed a great annual transplantation, but no one nation would finance it when all would benefit. By 1984 there may be more international cooperation and we may see both the very young fry from the Shelbourne 'factories' being carried long distances as well as a later stage transplantation à la Garstang.

I have already suggested* that the fisheries will be revolutionized by undersea men with tractor-trawls and other devices on the sea-bed, but I was then generally looking farther ahead. By 1984, however, I expect some enterprising company will not only be operating the first of these tractors but be making record catches by guiding them to the most productive grounds from fast one-man scouting submarines. There will be renewed outcries about over-fishing and a demand for greater international control. Extensive ecological studies by undersea naturalists will be started in preparation for the future weeding out of the principal competitors (starfish, etc.) for the food available to fish.

Now let us look at the great ocean spaces beyond the continental shelf, which are as yet hardly exploited except by line for tuna or by harpoon for whales. By 1984 various new kinds of fast mid-water trawls will have been invented for the capture of oceanic fish at various depths. There will be extensive fisheries for the red fish (*Sebastes marinus*) which the plankton recorder surveys across the Atlantic have now shown, by the capture of their young, to be abundant south of Iceland and Greenland. It appears likely that the widespread 'deep scattering layer' revealed by echo-sounders is usually due to shoals of small fish (particularly the luminous myctophids or lantern fish); if confirmed, these will certainly be harvested to be canned like sardines or converted into meal. Judging by the numbers of squid beaks found in the stomachs of sperm whales and other pelagic predators there must be vast stocks of these swift jet-propelled creatures awaiting attention; it would not surprise me if by 1984 there were fast self-powered, but unmanned, squid catchers being operated from parent ships.

* *New Scientist*, Vol. 7, p. 730.

Perhaps the most important development of all will be a new exploitation of the vast circumpolar Southern Ocean. Here, within the lifetime of many of us, the greatest whale fisheries have developed and, like their predecessors in the north, have been ruined by reckless fishing. Whilst the whale stocks have been dangerously reduced, their amazingly rich food, one species of planktonic shrimp, the krill, remains; it is there in almost unbelievable quantities. It feeds not only the whales, but much other Antarctic life as well: penguins, seals, and fish.

Dr George Forster, who accompanied Captain Cook on his voyage in *Resolution*, wrote in his account in 1777: ' If the northern ocean should ever be cleared of whales by our annual fisheries we might then visit the other hemisphere where these animals are known to be numerous.' On my return from the Antarctic in the *Discovery* Expedition of 1925–7, I referred in a lecture to the Royal Geographical Society to this passage by Forster; I then went on to say:

The great regions of summer plankton growth . . . are almost as striking as the ice-cap itself and as much stores of solar energy as the plains of wheat and grazing land of lower latitudes. It would not be a bolder prophecy than that of Forster to say that the time will come in the not too distant future when man will derive food and other power direct from these vast resources. (*Geographical Journal*, Vol. 72, p. 220.)

I think it likely that before 1984 we shall see huge steam, or diesel (or perhaps nuclear), 'artificial whales', gathering the krill by the shipload to add to the larders of the world. Harvesting the plankton has been tried in lower latitudes and, except by the Japanese, proved an economic failure; but the krill is quite different, it occurs in enormous, densely packed shoals. Perhaps in the form of meal it may be fed to and converted into other flesh. It is itself only one link in the food chain from the microscopic plants of the ocean; although only two inches long, the krill is the marine animal most like our sheep and oxen, grazing directly on the pastures. The whales it nourishes, mammals like ourselves, hold perhaps the record rate of growth. A baby blue whale is some 23 ft in length at birth and it has grown from the microscopic egg in only eleven months. Its mother has fed upon nothing but krill, and only for two thirds of the year; the baby itself, on the same diet, will be a strapping lad of 65 ft by its second birthday. Can we not save the starving children of the world with krill? I am sure we shall.

When this comes about the undernourished countries should be grateful for the enterprise that sent the Royal Research Ships *Disovery*, *Discovery II*, and *William Scoresby* on fifteen voyages south to provide information for a future regulation for the whale fisheries; and to the late Dr Stanley Kemp who planned it and all those who served under him in the rigours of the polar seas. It was only in November 1962 that the vast accumulation of knowledge on the distribution of the krill, based on over 12,000 plankton samples, was published in the huge *Discovery Report* (Vol. 32) by Dr James Marr. It will take time for the world to realize just what it has been given, but by 1984 the krill may be making the greatest addition to man's food supply of the century; the floating fish-meal factories off Peru will be nothing to the fleets of krill ships spread right round the world to the south.

Just as the tempo of exploitation will have risen, so will a greater support for general oceanography be forced upon the nations. The oceans will be covered by networks of observations from automatic recorders towed below the surface by commercial ships to track the changes in the sea like weather charting in the atmosphere. The old plankton recorders of today, now covering the North Atlantic, will be superseded by new ones charting other things as well as plankton. The Oceanographic Laboratory at Edinburgh, the headquarters of the survey, is now pioneering the design of these new machines which, by 1984, may be as common in the southern hemisphere as in the north.

WORKING DEEP IN THE SEA

by Edwin A. Link

Sea Diver Corporation, New York

I do not foresee man ever transferring his habitat from land to sea, for man is an air-breathing animal. It would take untold aeons for the necessary transmutations that would equip him like the whale or the porpoise. And even though the day may come sooner, when medical science finds a way to create a 'fishman' who obtains his oxygen through artificial gills, what man is there who would trade his birthright as a land creature to make his permanent home with the fishes?

However, I do envisage man spending ever greater lengths of time in the depths as he finds new and better means of conquering this alien environment. My experiments during the past year, in which mice have survived at pressure depths up to 3,600 feet, would indicate that by 1984 it will be an accepted practice for man to journey to this depth or perhaps even deeper. He will travel there in versatile, pressurized underwater vehicles which will allow him to emerge to work at such tasks as oil drilling, mining, fish culture, or the garnering of undersea crops.

He may live for days and weeks on the site of his labours in either permanent or temporary inflatable habitations such as I am presently developing. The area on which he works will be sheltered by heavy rubber tents which, when inflated, will empty themselves of water, thus creating a 'dry' atmosphere around the work site. No doubt this latter technique will, by then, have been adapted to such special tasks as painting or repairing a ship without having to remove it from the water.

The underwater vehicle which transports him back and forth will be pressurized so that decompression can be started immediately the ascent is begun, and an automatic joining to a comfortable decompression chamber at the surface will ensure safe and quick decompression.

Because by 1984 it will be commonplace for man to enter and work freely in the seas, we can foresee elaborate engineering developments scattered upon the ocean floor – underwater tunnels such as that contemplated beneath the English Channel, networks of telephone cables, and forests of oil derricks with interconnecting pipelines, all available for ready servicing. And when the depth becomes too great for man to survive, he will still be able to accomplish many of these tasks through the use of facile robots attached to the outside of the vehicles and responsive to guidance from within.

To construct these things, and to observe and explore the undersea life and physical environment, man might live in the sea for a month, even up to six months if necessary. I am sure there will also exist many underwater hostels where the enthusiastic skin diver can spend a week-end or even a couple of weeks of his vacation exploring his surroundings in wideflung areas of the seas. He will probably employ small one- and two-man vehicles to transport him, the Volkswagens of the deep.

However, in order to find his way about in the depths, it will first be necessary to develop new methods of navigation, and means of pinpointing his location in relation to his base of operations and his objective. To accomplish this, the operator of such a vehicle will probably have the equivalent of the present-day flyer's studies and training in getting about the skies.

By 1984, nuclear power will have been made available in sufficient quantity so that a goodly share of the oceans' commerce will have taken to the depths where there is no problem of inclement weather and heavy seas. This will be accomplished quite simply using portable, inflatable submarine tankers for the transportation of oil or other liquids, mineral ore, grains, cotton, fuel, milk, etc. These containers can then be deflated for return with a minimum of space and weight.

Such a method will also make it possible to exploit oil and mineral resources in arctic climates where there is presently no means of transporting these materials to areas of the world where they can be utilized. Successful voyages of nuclear submarines beneath the arctic ice have already proved the feasibility of such a system.

In twenty years man will have the technology and, if there is the need, will be constructing underwater dams in favourable positions to harness the strength of ocean currents and convert it to electrical energy. In addition to furnishing energy to sections of the world now deprived of it, this power can be used for changing salt water to fresh, and at the same time removing other valuable mineral contents. With plentiful power and fresh water available whole new areas will thus be converted from waste land to productive land to meet in part our growing need to feed a vastly expanding world population.

In another way, development of marine technology will serve the needs of the inhabitant of the land by influencing and controlling weather. It has already been suggested that, by deflecting ocean streams through the use of baffle dams, cold climates can be warmed, and arid deserts turned to livable environments. Such visionary changes, however, would have to be carried out on a worldwide basis with the cooperation of all nations involved.

A LONG VIEW FROM THE BEACH

by Dr Roger Revelle

Dean of Research, University of California

California, 1984. – To those of us who remember the hurricanes of the 1960s, with their grimly girlish names and their incredible viciousness, a certain excitement has gone out of life. It turned out that hurricanes could be prevented rather easily. All that was necessary was to lower the rate at which heat energy was delivered to the air from the condensation of water vapour. This had to be done in the ocean areas where hurricanes and typhoons were formed – the tropical Western Atlantic and Western Pacific, and the Indian Ocean off the Bay of Bengal.

Looking backward, it is clear that the breakthrough came with the development of a really coordinated system of orbiting weather satellites and instrumented ocean buoys, during the later 1960s. With these, it was possible to follow the conception, so to speak, and the embryonic stages of hurricanes. In all cases, these terrible storms began and grew over ocean areas where the water had absorbed more than the usual amount of solar energy, and where evaporation was abnormally high. Warm, humid air rose rapidly from the sea surface. As it rose, the water vapour condensed, transferring the heat of condensation to the air and causing it to rise still higher, which caused more condensation, more heating, and further upward motion. Colder, dryer air flowed inward to replace the rising air, and in turn it was heated by the warm sea, loaded with water vapour, and forced to rise. Gradually a vortex with a vertical axis was formed, the horizontal speed of the air motion increased enormously, the disturbance spread until it covered tens of thousands of square miles, and a new hurricane had begun its career of murder and destruction.

In 1968, teams of oceanographers and meteorologists in Japan, India, and the United States published nearly simultaneously a suggestion that the formation of hurricanes could be stopped if excess heating and evaporation of ocean waters in the regions of hurricane genesis could be eliminated. They thought this might be accomplished by spreading a thin layer of reflecting material on the sea surface, which would reflect part of the sunlight back to space before it had a chance to heat the water. Their hypothesis was attractive, but it could be tested only by a full-scale experiment, at a cost that was estimated, even by its advocates, at a billion dollars (it turned out to be two billion).

The experiment was finally conducted in 1973, under the auspices of the World Meteorological Organization and the Intergovernmental Oceanographic Commission. From the beginning of May till the end of August a fleet of British and American navy cargo ships, equipped with smoke generators, cruised back and forth over an area of a million square miles east of the Antilles. The smoke generators were used to spread a more or less continuous low cloud of micron-sized particles of aluminium oxide. These tended to stay at the surface long enough to reflect some sunlight, and by repeating the spreading process every three weeks, a good deal of energy absorption in the water was prevented.

The experiment was a complete success – not a single hurricane developed in the Atlantic during 1973 – but the cost was higher than the potential savings. An intensive search began for a reflecting substance that was insoluble and lighter than sea water, could be produced in very finely divided form, and above all could be very cheap if it were made in sufficiently large quantities. The best bet turned out to be an organic salt of magnesium. A panel of chemical engineers concluded that it could be produced for about a hundred dollars a ton, and that a ton would be sufficient to cover a square mile of sea water. But for even one hurricane-generating area a million tons of magnesium would be needed, and by 1973 world magnesium production had dwindled to about 100,000 tons a year. To extract the required amount of magnesium from sea water would mean processing about a billion tons of water, enough water, if it were fresh, to supply a city of six million people for a year.

Fortunately, the city of Los Angeles was just starting construction of a huge dual-purpose plant for simultaneously converting sea water to fresh water and generating very large blocks of electric power, using a nuclear reactor of unprecedented size (8,000 thermal megawatts) as the energy source. The plant was to be located in a sparsely settled part of the Californian coast, north of Point Conception. The quantity of fresh water to be produced was a billion gallons a day, very close to the amount of sea water required to obtain the needed million tons per year of magnesium. The city welcomed the idea of sharing its cost and of obtaining at the same time a firm market for some of its electric power.

The Californian plant went into full-scale production of fresh water, electric power, and magnesium in 1976. Similar plants were quickly constructed in two other water-short areas: Karachi and a location on the Texas coast south of Corpus Christi. During the past several years, fleets of twenty-five large bulk-carriers, equipped with smoke generators belching powdered magnesium compound, have patrolled the former hurricane-generating areas for a hundred days in late spring and summer. In Japan, Bengal, and the eastern United States, hurricanes are only a disagreeable memory. The cost of covering each area is about $120 million a year, far less than the damage formerly caused by hurricanes.

On the central California coast where the first huge nuclear plant was built, dramatic changes have occurred. Perhaps the most exciting is the development of recreational resources. Most of the heat generated by the plant must be carried off, of course, and enormous quantities of sea water are used to cool the working fluids. At the same time, nearly ten million tons a day of brine must be disposed of. The cooling water and the brine are carefully protected from radioactive contamination. On leaving the plant, the two kinds of water are mixed in the right proportions to be very close to the density of the coastal sea water, and spread by a long pipeline, submerged half a mile offshore, along forty miles of the coast. The result is that, throughout the year, the water temperature within several miles of the beach on this stretch of coast is 70–75° F., fifteen to twenty degrees warmer than it used to be. The oppressive summer fogs and cold onshore winds of former times have disappeared. Ten years ago, only the most masochistic swimmer ventured into the cold water; the few sandy beaches were nearly deserted, even in summer; and the country back of the coast was gradually becoming depopulated as farmers moved to the cities. Now a great new resort area is growing; middle-class real estate developments with names like New Riviera and Rancho del Mar are beginning to appear; and the waters are crowded with human beings and their conveyances.

The shore was formerly narrow, rocky, and virtually straight.

Now the state has constructed offshore islands and bars, break-waters, lagoons, and small curving bays. The actual length of shoreline, where sunbathers and swimmers, water skiers and surfers, sailors and sports fishermen, can cross the boundary from land to sea, has been tripled. Because of the warmer water, the fish population has drastically changed, very much for the better from the standpoint of the sports fishermen. Tuna, albacore, swordfish, marlin, and yellow tail are now abundant, and fields of giant kelp have grown up offshore.

The kelp itself is an ocean jungle in which little fish seek shelter and bigger ones their food. But beyond the kelp forest, the state fisheries agency has dumped piles of twisted, distorted wood, con-crete, and metal waste on the ocean floor, far beneath the surface. The magic changes of the sea have made these piles of junk into something rich and strange: abstract, unrecognizable structures that draw marine creatures like the lights of the city draw the country man. Because they concentrate marine life, these under-water structures actually result in a net increase of fish populations, to the joy of the sportsmen.

Looking beyond the kelp from the beach, we see a line of high platforms mounted on slender cylinders. We are told that these are fishing barges anchored above the underwater fish-concen-trating structures. Though the waves beat against them, the platforms and cylinders neither roll nor heave; they are as steady as if they were driven into the ocean floor. The cylinders are actually free-floating spar buoys, 200 to 300 ft long, with their lower ends below the zone of wave action, and so designed that they do not move with the waves. Seasickness, the curse of the occasional fisherman, never visits the spar buoymounted barges.

Behind the beach, we see a group of men with fishing gear climbing into a box-like contraption. Suddenly the box lifts about 6 in. off the ground, tilts slightly, and careers out to sea, rising smoothly over the breakers and waves, until it settles in the water next to one of the barges. It is a hovercraft, floating on its own cushion of fast-moving air, and driving forward by slight changes in the direction of air flow.

Near the horizon, far out beyond the line of anchored barges, a small tug is creeping southward at one or two miles per hour, ahead of a low, white, sinuous object. The object is at least five miles long, but it rises only about a foot above sea level. We are told that it is a giant plastic bag, 50 ft deep and 400 ft wide, filled with fresh water from the Columbia River. The water is being transported to Magdalena Bay on the peninsula of Baja California. Because the economy of the peninsula is based primarily on agriculture and tourism, and is on a far smaller scale than that of the Los Angeles area, it is more economical to obtain fresh water by transporting it from a distance than by distilling it from sea water in a large multi-purpose plant. Although the bag contains an enormous mass of water, over ten million tons, this would be only three days' supply for Los Angeles. The bag is fitted with an ingenious system of flaps, so that it is propelled southward by the ocean waves; the tug is simply there to steer it in the right direction.

Bringing our eyes back to the breaker zone, we are captivated by the sight of a group of children riding through the surf on the backs of tame porpoises. It is hard to tell who is having the most fun, the laughing, yelling children or the big grinning animals. Although the question of the potential level of intelligence of porpoises is still being argued, one of the remarkable accomplishments of animal psychology during the last twenty years has been the discovery of a means to domesticate and train these wonderful animals. The secret is Indian music – porpoises are apparently fascinated by its complex rhythms and intricate, repetitive melodies. An underwater loudspeaker connected to a phonograph playing recordings of Indian music quickly attracts a school of quietly listening porpoises. While they are under the music's spell it is easy to make friends with them, and later to use the music as a system of rewards in training them.

We see other children, and even some adults, covered from head to foot in plastic suits of a peculiar design. These are special swimming suits constructed to translate normal human leg motion into the highly effective wavy motions used by marine mammals in swimming. With these suits it is possible for a child, after a few lessons, to swim faster and farther than an Olympic champion who is using the traditional crawl stroke.

At the southern end of the forty mile strip of coast, a great industrial complex is growing around the nuclear power and water plant. Beside magnesium, rubidium and caesium are extracted from the sea water; chemical works based on these metals have been built, together with alloying and fabricating plants for the new uses of magnesium that have developed now that a steady, large supply is assured. Several deep-sea dredges are anchored offshore. They are discharging phosphate rock scraped from the banks off southern and lower California into a pipeline leading to a triple super-phosphate fertilizer plant. Bulk-carrying cargo submarines, their superstructures just awash, are unloading into other pipelines.

Every few days, a ship laden with concentrated ores of manganese, copper, nickel, and cobalt comes in from the new high-seas manganese-nodule fields. Despite the obvious potentialities of these vast deposits, the great mining companies made little attempt to exploit them until 1975. In that year the United Nations declared its jurisdiction over the ocean floor under the high seas and began to grant licences to private firms on a royalty basis for exclusive mining rights to accurately defined areas. The UN share of the returns from these enterprises has gone a long way towards solving its perennial financial problems.

Space vehicles have become so large that it is no longer possible to transport them on land. They are now assembled at coastal yards and launched on huge barges, essentially floating dry-docks, which are then towed out to a high-seas launching site. We see several of the enormous sheds under which these vehicles are being constructed.

Looking back, from 1984, over the past twenty years at the changes in our scientific understanding of the part of the earth that is covered with sea water, two areas seem particularly noteworthy: we have learned a good deal about how the ocean and the atmosphere act on each other; and we have gained completely new insight into the history of the ocean basins.

As I have already stated, a coordinated network of world-girdling weather satellites and deep-anchored ocean buoys was pretty well established before 1970. Many of the anchored stations were giant manned spar buoys similar to the seasick-proof fishing barges off the California coast. They had a double purpose; to take continuous records of changing oceanic and atmospheric conditions at a series of points over the ocean, and to detect and track submerged submarines. (This function was carried out under international agreement as one of the steps towards general disarmament. Because the spar buoys extended about 300 ft beneath the surface and did not move with the ocean waves, they were ideal for both underwater listening and echo-ranging.)

The satellites and the anchored buoys complemented each other. The satellites gave a complete global map of incoming and outgoing radiation and cloud cover, and a partial view of ocean surface temperatures; the buoys yielded a picture of the vertical exchanges of heat, water vapour, carbon dioxide, and momentum between the sea and the air, and how these affected the vertical distribution of oceanic and atmospheric temperatures and other properties.

It soon became evident that the amount of heat energy stored in the upper water layers, and the rate at which incoming solar energy was used to evaporate sea water, had a large-scale pattern which changed slowly but very significantly with changes in the pattern of cloud cover and winds. In turn, this oceanic pattern was of major importance in determining the locations of the fronts between air masses; the frequency, intensity, and tracks of storms, and the position and amplitude of the Rossby waves in the upper air. Although the basic hydrodynamics and thermodynamics of these relationships are still only partly understood, it has been possible to set up semi-empirical models, using large computers, which reproduce fairly accurately in a few hours the observed sequence of events over several months. This has led to great improvements in the accuracy and time horizon of long-range weather forecasting. It has been estimated that, in the United States alone, these improvements save upwards of two billion dollars a year. Farmers are able to adjust the times of planting and harvesting; oil companies can plan seasonal fuel transportation and storage; construction contractors can adapt their schedules to anticipated weather conditions; and government agencies are enabled to take forehanded measures for flood and drought protection.

The increase of about 15 per cent in atmospheric carbon dioxide from burning of coal, oil, and natural gas over the past twenty years is quite clearly having a marked effect on world climate, though not in any simple way. Some areas are becoming much warmer; others seem to be getting colder. In the 1960s about half the new carbon dioxide disappeared into the ocean. This fraction appears to be decreasing as warm surface water layers spread into higher latitudes in each hemisphere. We anticipate that climatic changes due to increases in atmospheric carbon dioxide will accelerate in the next few decades.

During the twenty years after the Second World War, several newly developed geophysical techniques were applied with great success to the exploration of the earth beneath the sea. These included recording echo-sounding to determine the shape of the sea floor and the topography of the hard reflecting layer beneath the unconsolidated sediment; seismic refraction and reflection measurements of the thickness and acoustic velocity of the crustal layers and the underlying mantle; measurements of variations in the acceleration of gravity and in the intensity of the earth's magnetic field; and determinations of the quantity of heat flowing from the interior of the earth. All of these techniques yielded valuable clues to the nature of the crust and mantle and the processes within the earth. But they gave no unique solutions, even in combination, rather only a range of possibilities.

This situation has been completely changed by the development of techniques for oceanic drilling. We are now able to sample at will, not only the entire layer of 'soft' sediments over the crustal rocks, but also the rocks themselves, down to and through the Mohorovicic discontinuity that was formerly thought to mark the boundary beneath the crust and mantle. New data are now being obtained very rapidly, and they are revealing a picture of such complexity that it has not yet been possible to arrive at many generalizations. We can say a few things with certainty, however. The only chemical difference between the rocks above and below the Mohorovicic discontinuity is in their water content; the overlying rocks are much higher in water and hence the minerals of which they are composed are still dense than the anhydrous minerals making up the rocks below the discontinuity. The true boundary between the crust and mantle seems to be at the top of the so-called 'third' layer. Over this layer, remnants of continental rocks have been found in several places, indicating that neither the oceans nor the continents have been 'permanent' features of the earth's surface. The evidence for break-up and drift of the continents seems ever more convincing.

One of the most exciting new discoveries is that at several places on the sea floor, under the blanket of soft sediments, old impact craters are preserved, resembling in most respects the craters of the moon, except that they are very much shallower because of the high gravitational force on the earth compared with the moon.

Weather and Climate

STEADY PROGRESS IN TECHNIQUES OF FORECASTING

by Sir Graham Sutton, F.R.S.

Director-General of the Meteorological Office

To foresee the progress of meteorology in the next twenty years is almost as difficult as forecasting weather a month ahead. Until about 1930 the instrumental aids available to the meteorologist were not much more than refined versions of those described by Robert Hooke in 1669. The science of the atmosphere relies upon continuous observation and in the last thirty years or so electronics has made all the difference. The task of the prophet is to estimate the impact of the knowledge so gained on the future of the science and the profession.

Observations

Our understanding of dynamical and physical processes in the atmosphere has greatly advanced since the upper levels became accessible with the development of the balloon radio-sonde and the radar wind-finder between 1930 and 1950. By 1984 we shall know much more about the structure and composition of the earth's gaseous envelope up to very high levels, for both the rocket-sonde and the meteorological satellite will have become commonplace by then. The World Meteorological Organization is now at the planning stage of the World Weather Watch. In the next twenty years, provided that the world remains comparatively peaceful, the present gaps in our knowledge of current weather over the huge oceanic areas (especially in the southern hemisphere) and sparsely populated regions (such as the deserts and tropical areas) will have been largely filled in. The automatic meteorological station is now a reality and observations of almost all the elements of weather can be made in uninhabited areas and transmitted to collecting centres. The technical problems have been solved and the question is simply one of cost.

Automation already plays a large part in the work of the major national services and much of the soul-destroying labour of collecting and analysing observations by hand has disappeared. By 1984 the communications network will feed in data at extremely high speed direct to computing systems, where the information will be stored in a form suitable for answering queries or providing basic data for research. If national pride can be overcome, it is possible that countries will relinquish their own climatological centres in favour of a few large international data-collecting and processing institutes to which problems can be fed in and replied to by cable with the minimum of human intervention. Without such rationalization the potentialities of the World Weather Watch cannot be realized to the full.

Forecasting

Today, much of the effort of the national meteorological services goes to provide forecasts of high-level winds and temperatures for aviation. By 1984 most of this work will have been automated and the laborious plotting of charts by hand and the endless drawing of lines will be memories only. The forecast charts will come direct from the computer, which will also do the necessary preliminary analysis of the observations. Already forecasts of wind and upper troposphere conditions produced by dynamical methods have attained an accuracy better than that achieved by experienced meteorologists using time-honoured 'hand' methods. In the next twenty years all forecast charts will be produced in this way and the 'routine forecaster' will be more of a research scientist, chiefly employed in devising methods of improving the range and reliability of his predictions. Local short-term forecasts will be greatly improved with the extension of the horizon of observation by weather radars and by meteorological satellites giving almost continuous cover of most parts of the earth.

This, however, does not mean that the problems of short-range weather forecasting are likely to be completely solved in the next twenty years. The methods indicated above are capable of producing (but at considerable cost) detailed and substantially accurate forecasts of weather for a few hours ahead. For longer periods, say 24 to 48 hours ahead, the heterogeneity of weather (especially precipitation) and the complexities of the problem arc such that it is difficult to foresee very striking advances in the precision and reliability of general forecasts. It seems that, in the temperate latitudes, there will always be a residual uncertainty in a forecast of weather for a day or two ahead. We have to reckon with what is essentially a fluid in turbulent motion for which the meteorologist has to predict, in considerable detail, the behaviour of individual large eddies. What can be confidently expected is that the occurrence of major errors will be greatly reduced, but the weather forecast will still be basically a statement of probabilities.

The prospects for long-range forecasts are less certain. These are predictions of transient climatic fluctuations, such as a wet August or (as in 1964) an unusually dry winter. The main problem here is to find the cause of such deviations. We can now describe in much detail the course of the severe winter of 1962-3 and can explain *how* it occurred; but we can do little more than guess *why* it occurred. We cannot yet trace a cause-and-event sequence in such large deviations and cannot identify any event, either terrestrial or extra-terrestrial, of which we can say with confidence 'Here it began'. Even so, it is reasonable to expect that by 1984 the art will have progressed so far that forecasts covering the coming month (or even the season) will be available for most of the extra-tropical regions and that they will have attained a useful consistent accuracy. Progress in this exceptionally difficult problem must, in the long run, depend upon the establishment of more objective methods for which at present theory is lacking.

Scientific theory

The advances made in the application of dynamical theory to short-range predictions, particularly in the upper air, have already been mentioned. Here one can confidently foresee steady progress and by 1984 the mathematical theory of the formation and motion of depressions and anticyclones should be well established. The Meteorological Office has now begun a detailed study of the dynamics and thermodynamics of frontal systems and of the quantitative prediction of precipitation. These are formidable problems, calling for the use of the largest computers, but there is no reason to believe that substantial success will not be achieved in the next twenty years, either in Britain or elsewhere.

On the larger scale, one can expect considerable progress towards the solution of the major problem of meteorology, that of explaining quantitatively the genesis and maintenance of the general circulation of the atmosphere and the main climatic zones of the earth. When such a theory is established it will be possible to proceed to the even more difficult mathematical study of the perturbations of the circulation that give rise to the transient climate fluctuations which are the preoccupation of the long-range forecaster, and also to discuss realistically even greater problems. It is still unknown why in regions such as north-west Europe the weather of one year differs so much from another. By 1984 we should have decided whether there are genuine external 'causes' of these variations (such as the sun or the oceans) or whether they simply illustrate the variety of modes of motion that the atmosphere can adopt without any specific external cause. How far it will be possible to advance towards a reliable system of long-range forecasting must largely depend upon the answers to these questions.

On a smaller (but still important) scale we can expect the origin of thunderstorm electricity to be settled and a quantitative theory of the thunderstorm to be established. The tropical hurricane will be better understood so that ample warning can be given of its birth and history.

Control of weather and climate

We know, with fair certainty, the orders of magnitude of the energy exchanges in most atmospheric systems, from the general circulation to the local thunderstorm. The kinetic, thermal, and electrical energy of a typical thunderstorm is comparable with that released in a megaton bomb explosion and it is well established that between 1,000 and 2,000 thunderstorms occur in the atmosphere at any time. It is thus unlikely that the circulation can be forced into a desired mode by the local application of man-made forces and in the present state of knowledge it is impossible to predict with confidence the final outcome of any such attempt.

As yet there is no certainty that any method of modifying weather or climate on a large scale is likely to succeed, and no attempt now would be worth the risk and expense. One doubts if this situation will have changed radically by 1984. There was some hope that atmospheric processes of an unstable character or dependent upon triggering (e.g. rain formation in some clouds) could be initiated by relatively small effort, but this now seems doubtful. No economic gain has been definitely demonstrated in trials so far.

Weather modification must remain the greatest uncertainty of all, so much so that it seems safe to prophesy that in 1984 British weather will be much as it always has been.

THE WORLD WEATHER SATELLITE SYSTEM

by Dr S. Fred Singer

National Weather Satellites Center, U.S. Weather Bureau

Florida, 1984. – Only thirty years ago the concept of an artificial earth satellite which would carry instruments and perform some useful function was looked upon with great amusement and disbelief, even by the scientific community. But six years later, on 1 April 1960, a small beginning was made when the first weather satellite, *Tiros*, was launched from Florida and demonstrated the immense value of satellites for the spotting of dangerous storms and for general weather prediction.

Just twenty years ago, a plan for an operational weather satellite system was made firm, and shortly thereafter the first such system came into being; it was based on a modification of the *Tiros* satellite which, in the meantime, had proven itself to be very successful and reliable. By 1970, a second generation satellite took its place with vastly augmented functions; and about five years ago our present system, a third-generation satellite, came into being. It would be difficult to imagine the world today without this satellite system. It is saving lives and property by predicting severe weather conditions; it is advancing economic operations everywhere; and it is generally contributing to the well-being of the citizens of the world.

It is important to realize how the functions of the weather satellite system have grown to encompass the monitoring of all kinds of data about our environment, not only the atmosphere, but also the earth, the oceans, and space. It is important to realize, too, how economically useful the many ancillary functions have become, such as navigational services, geodesy, and data relay.

Our World Weather Satellite System uses three satellites in polar orbits at an altitude of about 2,000 miles. Their orbital planes are spaced 120° apart so that they cover different regions of the world at different times and provide more or less continuous observations. The satellites themselves are large and heavy, and nuclear-powered, in order to run the sensors, on-board computers, recorders, transmitters, and so forth; their operating life, safeguarded by stand-by circuitry, is about ten years.

The instruments carried by the satellites for detecting radiation emanating from below include advanced television cameras which can 'see' the clouds day or night, infra-red sensors to measure heat radiations, and microwave sensors to measure emitted radio waves. All of these radiations come either from the surface of the earth, from its atmosphere, or from material in the atmosphere such as clouds. Through specialized sensors and computers, the satellite is able to measure the vertical pattern of temperatures of the atmosphere; it can deduce the winds and other important meteorological quantities such as humidity; and it measures the content of important atmospheric constituents such as ozone and water vapour. In short, the satellite gathers all the data which are important for making accurate weather prediction possible.

The quantities which cannot be directly measured by the satellite sensors are measured by ground stations and ocean buoys; thousands of these are distributed all over the earth; they operate automatically, radioing their readings to the satellite as it passes overhead. The satellite stores these additional data on magnetic tape and its computer integrates them with the data which are observed by the satellite's sensors.

All of the data are then spewed out, once per orbit, to central receiving stations located near the North Pole. One of these giant stations was constructed in 1963 near Fairbanks, Alaska (serving America and East Asia), one was built in Scandinavia, and a third one in northern Siberia. From these receiving stations data links go back to the four complex data-processing and analysis facilities, in Washington, Tokyo, Geneva, and Moscow, where high-speed electronic computers dissect and reassemble the nearly 10,000 million bits of data which pour in every day, and put them into a format from which skilled meteorologists produce forecasts of global weather.

In addition to data collection, the satellite is also used for data relaying. After the forecast charts are produced at the data-processing station, the analysis is sent back to the receiving station and from there transmitted up to the satellite; the satellite in turn carries this global analysis to all of the weather stations throughout the world, to ships at sea, and to anyone who wants to tune in to its message. The satellite also provides a direct readout of meteorological data for the particular area over which it passes. The forecaster then combines this local cloud picture with the global analysis.

A supplementary meteorological satellite system has been developed in connexion with the so-called 'synchronous' or 'stationary' communication satellite; the combining of functions has been shown to lead to a considerable saving in costs. A satellite in equatorial orbit at an altitude of 22,000 miles moves with the same rotational period as the earth and appears to be stationary above a particular point on the equator. The Syncom system, used extensively for transcontinental communications, has proved extremely valuable also for certain specialized meteorological applications: short-lived weather phenomena, small severe storms, tornadoes, and the like can be missed by the polar-orbiting World Weather Satellite System, but synchronous satellites can, on demand, keep any specific area of the globe under continuous surveillance.

In addition to observing the clouds and the atmosphere, the satellite system has proved itself outstandingly useful for monitoring other phenomena on the earth's surface. It can observe the distribution of ice, and this information has been used to make ice forecasts and to direct icebreakers and ice reconnaissance aircraft. It measures the distribution of snowfall and precipitation; from these data the amount of snow which will melt is calculated and hydrological forecasts are prepared for managers of flood-control projects, irrigation reservoirs, and for agricultural planners.

The satellite can observe drought conditions and flood

conditions, the areas of the world under cultivation, and even the state of the crops; it thus produces all of the basic data which are important in economic forecasting, and thereby has made possible more efficient planning and more efficient use of the world's food supply.

The infra-red sensors of the satellite monitor the world's oceans and the meandering of ocean currents; a technique for computing the distribution of fish has been deduced and has made possible the more effective utilization of the ocean's resources. Scientific 'farming' of the oceans is now becoming a practical enterprise.

Disaster warning services based on satellites are now quite well developed. The satellite is able to spot forest fires and other conflagrations in their incipient stages and produce early warnings which prevent the great economic losses from fires that get out of control. The same sensors monitor the activity of volcanoes and give warning of impending eruptions. Satellite cameras can track clouds of desert locusts swarming across Africa and Asia and alert the locust fighters to get their planes ready. At high altitudes the satellite monitors the motions of icebergs and warns shipping.

With radio sensors the satellite monitors the earth's ionosphere and uses this information to predict the propagation conditions for long-distance radio communications; with instruments turned upward the satellite monitors the sun and obtains data which are necessary for the forecasting of solar eruptions, which in turn affect communications services on the earth.

The satellite records changes in the earth's magnetic field, in the intensity of high-energy particles, and in other space phenomena, which together comprise the inputs for an extra-terrestrial 'weather' forecasting system. The satellite also picks up astronomical and geophysical data from observatories around the world and adds these to the data measured directly by the satellite. Extra-terrestrial 'weather' forecasts can then be prepared to aid in planning manned voyages to the moon and to other planets.

The satellite carries a flashing light, not only to aid in its tracking, but also to provide a convenient means for geodesists and cartographers to measure distances between points on the earth with extreme accuracy. For less accurate use, the satellite carries a simple radio transmitter whose 'doppler shift', when measured on the ground, can be used to infer the position of the ground receiving station. In other words, the satellite supplies a simple but effective navigational system. All merchant vessels, aircraft, and even many yachts now carry the very simple receiving equipment which makes all-weather day-or-night navigation possible.

These are just some of the more important economic applications of a satellite system which was originally designed for weather reconnaissance but which can also fulfil many other useful functions. The economic impact of the World Weather Satellite System has, in fact, become so great that it has affected the political thinking of many nations. It has proved itself a most valuable tool in protecting citizens of all countries against the destructive influences of the environment. It was therefore recognized in the late 1960s that this immensely useful system must be protected in the event of a conflict between nations. Later, it was placed under the control of the United Nations.

After 1984

I hope I may be forgiven for speculating about the future, up to the end of the century. Some very challenging scientific analyses of world climate have been published recently, using about twenty years' worth of global satellite data. The agreement between independent investigators on different continents is very gratifying; it is quite evident that extra-terrestrial influences on the upper atmosphere do produce important 'triggering' effects on weather near the ground. Clearly, it will soon become possible to determine the nature and also the origin of climatic fluctuations and to understand much better why it is that climates vary, both in the short-term and on a longer-term basis. It is exciting to consider the possibility of finding the cause of the ice ages, which constitute extreme fluctuations in the climate. This information will come partly from the weather satellite system, but partly also from a better understanding of the history of the oceans and of the earth, and from refined astronomical observations.

Once a better understanding of the climates has been obtained, the road would be clear for climate control, or 'planetary engineering' as it might properly be called. Over the past two decades, various attempts have been made to modify weather on a small scale. Now experiments will be made to trigger changes in the climate.

But in order to check whether these changes are in fact occurring and to determine their exact course we need highly refined observations; many of these will be carried out by a specially constructed orbiting meteorological and geophysical observatory. I would visualize this observatory satellite as manned, since many of the instruments may require continuous adjustment, and since special observations may be called for which cannot be anticipated. Furthermore, the instrumentation will be so complex that an unmanned observatory is simply not feasible from an economic point of view; its reliability would become too low. The observatory satellites may be either continually manned, or perhaps manned only during the special occasions when 'planetary engineering' tests are undertaken.

It is clear that these attempts to modify the environment in which man lives on our planet will be fraught with great risks, but it is clear also that they will be among the most exciting and promising ventures of the last part of this century. Very likely, all of these activities will again be carried out under the supervision of a world body, such as the United Nations, in order to avoid any unilateral actions that might be detrimental to specific countries. Today, in 1984, a good beginning has been made in climate modification experiments; we can therefore predict with some degree of confidence that man will soon control his environment on the earth to suit his convenience and to achieve a better life.

METEOROLOGY AND HUMAN ACTIVITY

by D. A. Davies

Secretary-General of the World Meteorological Organization

Man, like all living creatures, is influenced by his environment – the atmosphere. By using his superior intelligence he has, however, become somewhat less dependent upon his environment than other creatures; indeed, he already possesses the means of escaping completely from it by underwater and outer-space vehicles. Nevertheless, the scope of normal human activities is still largely determined and controlled by conditions in the atmosphere and will continue to be for many years to come. In this article we consider the extent to which those atmospheric phenomena which comprise the weather and climate will influence human activities in 1984.

It seems necessary to consider first whether by 1984 the climate itself will have changed. The long-term fluctuations in climatic conditions have played a predominant part in human development throughout the ages. In terms of the time-scale of such fluctuations, a period of twenty years is, however, extremely small and, while there are some indications that there may be a slight general cooling of the atmosphere in the coming years, for the purpose of this article it is assumed that as far as natural changes are concerned, the atmosphere will still be behaving in very much the same way then as it does now.

Whether man, by accident or by intent will, by 1984, have altered or have the means of altering natural processes to such an extent as to change significantly the weather and climate is, of course, also relevant; but as the other contributors discuss this subject it is not pursued further here. It is also relevant to consider whether there will be any significant improvements in techniques for short- and long-range weather prediction in twenty years' time. The article by Sir Graham Sutton (page 115) answers this question.

Let us begin by considering what might be called the three traditional applications of meteorology – services to the general public, to aviation, and to shipping.

It is safe to predict that forecasts for the general public will still be required in 1984. Indeed, the trend is for the general public to become more 'weather-conscious' and increasingly to use forecasts in making personal arrangements. Apart from any overall improvement in the accuracy of weather forecasts, the most significant development in the twenty years ahead will probably be in improved methods of enabling any individual to obtain special advice for his special need. Such developments as weather 'shops', meteorological telephone systems, meteorological programmes on television and radio have already demonstrated clearly the tremendous interest in and need for weather information on the part of the general public. In twenty years' time such systems will no doubt be extended and improved.

There has always been a very close association between meteorology and aviation and throughout the world an intricate and accurate meteorological service for aviation has been developed. Just as the system has recently had to be modified to meet the needs of the present-day jet aircraft, so during the next twenty years the system will need to be modified further to meet the needs of supersonic aircraft which will, no doubt, by that time be circling the earth at stratospheric heights. Already the meteorological requirements of such aircraft have been discussed and appropriate adjustments to the world system of aeronautical meteorology are being planned. For example, the prediction of rain and hail during the climb to or descent from the cloudless stratospheric cruising level will take on a new importance because of their serious effect on aircraft flying at very great speeds. Possibly information on ozone, ultra-violet radiation, cosmic radiation, and artificial radioactivity at the cruising heights may be required, as well as the more conventional type of data. There seems to be little doubt that the meteorologist will, as in the past, keep pace with the demands of the aviator.

As regards shipping, the international system whereby any ship in any ocean of the world can obtain weather information from a prescribed shore station will no doubt continue and be adjusted as necessary to meet changing requirements. Forecasts of gales and fog, warnings of hurricanes and typhoons, etc. will still be of significance. Ship routing on long voyages will take into account weather conditions much more than at present, with consequent benefits to speed and comfort.

Among the other applications of meteorology, two will play an increasingly important role in the future and may become of prime importance in many countries: they are the applications to agriculture and water resources development. In the developing countries of the world, agriculture is likely to be for many years the main factor in the determined efforts of these countries to achieve economic self-sufficiency. Moreover, the need to produce more food for the rapidly increasing world population will incite all countries to look to their agricultural practices in order to increase production for their own needs or to help to meet the needs of others. In the planning of such activities, agro-climatic studies will need to play a prominent role, as well as special studies of rainfall and run-off for irrigation purposes. Any improvements in long- or short-range forecasting will, of course, be of importance in farming operations. Meteorology will also play an increasing role in the fight against agricultural pests and diseases, the incidence of many of which is known to be dependent upon meteorological conditions.

In addition to its importance for agricultural purposes, hydrometeorology is likely to become increasingly important for questions related to water utilization in general, including hydroelectricity and water supplies for human and industrial consumption. Most countries are already well aware of the dangers of the planning of large national development schemes involving water utilization without a careful study of the rainfall and run-off statistics. Evaporation losses from reservoirs are significant in some regions and the present means of reducing such losses on a small scale may well be extended to large-scale operations by 1984. Flood-forecasting techniques will become increasingly important and improved techniques will undoubtedly be developed. Hydro-meteorology will also play an increasing role in navigation on internal waterways and in dealing with water-pollution problems.

The applications of meteorology to industry have never been so obvious as the applications already mentioned; nevertheless, they are by no means negligible and will no doubt expand. I have already referred to water supplies for industry. Industrial air pollution will continue to be a problem and will tend to expand geographically as many of the less-developed countries become more industrialized. Short-range weather prediction for such things as the assessment of the load on electricity supplies will be increasingly needed in major population centres. The use of wind and solar radiation as sources of energy will probably increase.

The applications of meteorology mentioned above are certainly the main ones but they are by no means exhaustive. Much could be said on such additional matters as meteorology in relation to human health (the influences of weather and climate on the occurrence of disease, etc.); to building design and construction; to tourism and recreation; and even to insurance schemes. No doubt the next twenty years will see advances in all these fields. Mention might also have been made of the uses of meteorology in outer space exploration, particularly in the prediction of atmospheric conditions for the critical stages of launching and climb through the earth's atmosphere and for the return to earth of astronauts. This, of course, is quite apart from the highly important new observational tool, the meteorological satellite.

To sum up, it may be said that by 1984 there is likely to be a substantial all-round increase in the direct practical benefits derived from the application of meteorological knowledge and skills to many fields of human activity. A significant development will undoubtedly be the increased recognition of the importance of meteorology to economic development, particularly in relation to agriculture and water utilization. New developments such as artificial satellites present unprecedented possibilities to the meteorologist and much will depend upon his ability to use these to the full in advancing his basic understanding of the atmosphere.

Chemicals

PLENITUDE FROM PETROLEUM

by Professor H. W. Slotboom

Scientific Adviser, Shell International Research Mij. N.V.

Will there be enough oil in 1984 for us to talk usefully about the prospects for its products? Experts in the oil industry say yes; they are confident that the present reserves of crude oil, plus additional sources which are likely to be discovered as a result of current exploration, are adequate to allow consumption to grow, even at the present rate, until 1984 and even beyond.

Today, more than 90 per cent of the crude oil produced is processed into products which provide roughly half of the world's total energy. The rest – less than 10 per cent – is converted into a wide range of other products. They include lubricating oils, paraffin wax, and asphaltic bitumen, as well as 'petro-chemicals'.

Nearly 20 million tons of organic chemicals from petroleum will be made in the free world during 1964, and it does not seem over-optimistic to forecast a quantity of 100 million tons by 1984. This increase will be stimulated by lower manufacturing costs, thanks to scientific advances in the design and operation of new processing units. Oil and chemicals manufacturing plants in 1984 will have larger units and fully-integrated control systems, with computers to make the decisions for economic operation.

In the energy field during the next twenty years the overall position of petroleum will not be affected other than marginally, although the fuel pattern is likely to change. The use of nuclear reactors in electric power stations and in ships may check the growth rate in the use of heavy fuel, and cheaper electricity may well cause the growth curve for domestic petroleum fuel for central heating to flatten out; but on the other hand there is likely to be steady growth in the utilization of petroleum in metallurgy, particularly for reducing iron ore.

Petroleum fuels for motor-cars, heavy vehicles, and aeroplanes will not be affected by the above trends. The new type of fuel which is being developed for supersonic jet aircraft will be hydrocarbon-based; so undoubtedly will be the fuel for any of the new devices for the generation of automotive power which may emerge from current research and development activities. An example is the fuel cell.

The combination of piston engine, hydrocarbon fuel, and petroleum lubricant still holds a great deal of potential for further improvements in efficiency and convenience. As a welcome offshoot of such improvements we may expect the world to be a quieter and cleaner place in 1984.

The utilization of petroleum-based products outside the energy field goes back to the beginning of the oil industry. The manufacture and use of special hydrocarbon solvents, asphaltic bitumen as a cheap plastic material for road-making and for hydraulic and industrial applications, and paraffin wax for waterproofing packing paper have gone through a long period of continuous technological development, which will continue.

The marriage between the oil and chemical technologies, of which petrochemicals are the offspring, promises to be still more fruitful in the next twenty years.

Conventional oil products, such as fuels, are tending to become more and more 'chemical', as the result of increased conversion of hydrocarbons in the manufacturing processes and the adding of special non-hydrocarbon chemicals to introduce new desirable qualities in performance. It is very likely that the engine fuels of 1984 will contain completely new types of chemical additives, and the motor lubricants may well be entirely synthetic.

Thanks to its cheapness and reliability of supply, petroleum is becoming a more and more versatile material for chemical products which have long been obtained from other sources. Examples are non-hydrocarbon solvents, detergents, and synthetic rubber. Today the oil industry – once a source of aliphatics – also produces cheap aromatics: in the U.S.A. the majority of the aromatics used by the chemical industry come from oil instead of, as formerly, coal.

The marriage has, above all, opened up the way to completely new chemical products for a much wider range of uses. Various cheap and versatile building blocks for synthetic plastics and fibres can be made from petroleum, notably 'unsaturated' (chemically reactive) hydrocarbons which can be combined with other reactive groups. At the same time, progress in chemistry has supplied industry with new means of sticking these building blocks together to form predetermined 'stereo-specific' molecular structures. This has already led to the manufacture of a challenging new plastic, polypropylene, as well as to the industrial manufacture of natural rubber on the basis of isoprene derived from petroleum.

The combination of this range of building blocks and the assorted variety of chemical techniques has great possibilities for the development of new plastic materials for use in clothing, packaging, building, and household appliances. The realization of these possibilities will largely determine how far the world's needs for more, better, and cheaper housing will be met in 1984. Supersonic flight and space travel call for special tailor-made synthetic materials.

The fact that the development of such materials is still largely based on trial and error will greatly stimulate scientific research in order to obtain better knowledge of the relationship between the molecular structure of such materials and their performance; and it is certainly imaginable that in the next twenty years new basic principles for the creation of plastic construction materials will emerge.

Not only science, but also psychology will influence the extrapolation of present trends into the plastic materials of 1984. People's likes and dislikes will stimulate the development of new kinds of attractiveness in appearance adapted to the 'nature' of the new materials as being different from the familiar ones: ceramics, wood, metal, and textiles. The 1984 patterns of form and colour in the uses of plastic materials will probably be very different from the present ones.

Petrochemicals will also be used more and more in the field of public health, particularly in those applications where cheapness and volume are important. The protection of crops and livestock against pests and diseases is largely based on petrochemicals. Here, as in the field of plastics, science has discovered potent new methods of analysing and synthesizing complex molecular structures, such as those involved in the metabolism of animals and plants. The great challenge is to understand the relationship between physico-chemical structure and biological activity of specific chemicals. The future control of diseases of plants and animals will be based on increased understanding of the biological activity of specific chemical structures and on better harmony between the chemical and the biological approach.

The chemical synthesis of components for animal food, such as amino acids, has already resulted in the industrial manufacture of lysine and methionine from petroleum. Biosynthesis is on the way to making petroleum a starting material for protein production.

More than in any other field, the use of chemicals for biological purposes will depend on the public understanding and acceptance of both the benefits and the implications of scientific progress. Therefore education and enlightenment of the public – to combat the collective traumata which so much hamper the progress of developing countries and even affect developed areas of the world – will determine the 1984 picture just as much as will progress in science and technology.

Inasmuch as the foregoing constitutes a scientific programme for the next twenty years, it may not have the glamour of a journey to the moon. However, its realization will require as much effort from scientists of many disciplines, and would it be less stimulating?

Of one thing I am sure: a theme to ponder about in 1984 will be 'Chemicals in 2004', as much as 'Chemicals in 1984' is today.

CHEMISTRY AND LIVING ORGANISMS

by Professor Koichi Yamada

Department of Agricultural Chemistry, University of Tokyo

What will happen in the next twenty years in those fields of chemistry which are particularly related to food and pharmaceuticals? I would like to discuss the possibilities from the viewpoint of one who is engaged in research in industrial microbiology.

It is said that the world's population will increase to as much as five billion by 1984, and it is going to be a difficult problem to feed this increasing population. Yet how serious will the food deficiencies be in practice ? For reasons that I shall explain, I think that the situation will not be as bad as has been predicted.

In the first place, the yields per acre of farm products will be tremendously increased by means of improved technology, whether in soil science, horticulture, or fertilizers. Secondly, new pesticides will result in an almost complete elimination of crop losses from pests and disease, thus raising the useful yield of crops. Newly discovered synthetic pesticides and antibiotics will be even more effective in preventing wastage of fruits and vegetables than the well-tried materials. Following in the wake of the gibberellins and other remarkable substances, a series of new plant-growth promotion factors will appear for enlarging the size of individual plants. Another new method of controlling the size of plants will involve the use of improved growth retardants, which will be sprayed on plants to restrict their size but stimulate the production of grain seed.

The approach whereby micro-organisms themselves serve as food will have significant bearing in changing primitive agricultural methods towards new industrial techniques. For example yeasts, moulds, and fungi will be produced in deep culturing tanks with constant yield throughout the year. Unlike conventional fermentation methods, which depend almost entirely on carbohydrate sources, this new process will also utilize hydrocarbons such as kerosene and petroleum waste. Bacteria which can photosynthesize their own food or live on waste organic material will assume increased importance.

Progress in the studies of food taste and flavour, especially in identification of the chemical structures of flavouring compounds, will open a new horizon in food synthesis and food processing. For example a process like the maturing of whisky, which now requires many years, will be shortened to a matter of a few hours. Food production can meet the demands resulting from increased populations, if people will accept new types of food.

Now let us see what further benefits microbiology may bring in the pharmaceutical field. Firstly, cancer may be controlled by a new series of antibiotics; the problems of side reactions caused by high dosage will be solved. Anti-viral antibiotics are new tools which may assist in the eventual elimination of cancer. Various new vitamins and hormones will be discovered through future progress in the investigations of microbiological growth factors, in micro-analysis of animal and plant substances, and in tissue culture. With better understanding of the mechanisms involved in hormone metabolism, it will become possible to control biological development by chemicals, not only in such phases as germination and vernalization, but also in all aspects of morphology. Misuse of this approach, however, could result in serious disasters to health. Yet human wisdom will make beneficial use of this approach to prolong human life. Furthermore, new drugs for mental disease and safe birth-control agents may be produced from micro-organisms.

The most remarkable progress will be seen in the field of enzymes, the promoters of natural chemical processes and the regulators of metabolism. Physiologically active substances concerned in enzymatic systems will be produced artificially by the synthesis of proteins. Also the structure of active portions of various enzyme molecules, and the vital sequences of amino acids involved, will be identified. These advances will lead us eventually to the successful synthesis of enzymes. Synthetic enzymes having lower molecular weight will be developed as drugs for injection without causing side-effects.

Finally, what will be the nature of fermentation industry in 1984? New substances will be produced by chemical transformation through the combined efforts of well-advanced petro-chemical technology and industrial microbiology. Substances of higher molecular weight which are generally difficult to synthesize by ordinary means will also be produced. Attention will be focused upon studies of photosynthetic and heat-resistant micro-organisms, with the rapid advancement of microbial synthesis utilizing the by-products of petroleum. In essence, microbiology will help to ensure that, by 1984, human beings can be freed from disease and can enjoy a life of prosperity blessed with an abundance of food, with health, and with longevity.

THE ASCENDANCY OF GIANT MOLECULES

by Professor Giulio Natta

Institute of Industrial Chemistry, Milan Polytechnic

I shall attempt here to examine the likely industrial developments in giant synthetic molecules during the next twenty years. By then, their importance will be far greater than it is even today. The field of macromolecular chemistry embraces natural substances in everyday use (such as proteins, carbohydrates, natural rubber, wood, fibres such as cotton, wool, and silk) and several natural products that are very important both from the biological and industrial points of view (notably nucleic acids and enzymes).

It is only in the last few decades that, thanks to the progress of chemistry, it has become possible to produce, by synthesis, macromolecular substances that can compete with, and sometimes even show better properties than, natural substances.

The recent discovery of the 'stereo-specific' polymerization processes has enlarged the possibilities in synthesizing macromolecular products (plastics, synthetic fibres, and synthetic rubbers). These processes enable us to link small molecules together in a manner that yields giant molecular structures having a high chemical and steric (three-dimensional) regularity, with a pre-determined type of symmetry and hence pre-determined properties. By such means we can synthesize products having the same constitution as the natural polymers and also make similar products that do not exist in nature.

The production of synthetic macromolecular products has increased enormously in the past ten years: indeed, no other branch of the chemical industry has made such a big leap.

While it may be possible to foresee the progress of other branches of industry in the next twenty years by extrapolating from the statistics of previous decades, where macromolecules are concerned we cannot do so because the big advances are so recent. Nevertheless, we can make predictions about the main fields.

Plastics

The world production of each of the most important synthetic polymers known at present – notably polyethylene, polypropylene, polyvinylchloride, styrene polymer and copolymer, phenolics, and polyesters – can be expected to reach several million tons per year. The quantities of articles made of plastics will greatly exceed those made of light metals. The possibilities are numberless; I can only give some examples of the widening use of plastics.

In the packaging industry, the plastics will surpass all other materials. Plastics with high melting points (polypropylene, for example) will allow the production of sterilized packages; thus metal cans will be largely replaced by opaque or transparent boxes made of plastics.

A great part of the building materials for houses (especially for prefabricated houses) will consist of plastics: for instance, more or less transparent plastics covers will substitute for tiles. Partition walls will be made of expanded plastics, exploiting their lightness and their heat and sound insulation. Furniture will be mostly made of plastics, rather than of the more expensive wood and metals.

The use of plastics in this field is presently limited by the capacity of the moulding machines; in particular, injection-moulding machines can handle no more than 15 kg in a single shot. But, within twenty years, it will be certainly possible to produce articles of several tens of kg, either by new types of moulding machines or by quite different processes.

Most, if not all, of the water pipes in houses will be made of plastics, being lighter and more readily shaped for particular needs. Similarly, in agriculture, light plastics pipes, fitting more easily the irregularities of the terrain, will be used instead of metal ones for irrigation. Artificial ponds will be created on sand and on permeable soils, by the laying down of weldable plastics films.

As for greenhouses, plastics will replace metals and wood for the frames, as well as glass for the transparent parts. As a result of low cost, greenhouses will be more widely used than today. Films of plastics will be used to protect several crops (from strawberries to grapes) for the sake of quicker ripening. In the case of vines, they will reduce or eliminate the need for the present expensive chemical treatments.

Textiles

Highly crystalline and very light fibres can now be obtained from stereoregular hydrocarbon macromolecules. For instance, polypropylene of high steric purity is made from propylene produced from petroleum at very low cost; with this polymer one can manufacture textile fibres that are very light (density 0.90–0.92) and have mechanical and thermal properties better than those of many other filaments. Large-scale production of these polypropylene fibres will bring the price down to a level defying all competition, even from cotton.

When used for clothes, polypropylene yields for a given weight a greater volume of fabric – 12.5 per cent more than for nylon, 50 per cent more than for PVC, and 70 per cent more than for cotton. Thus it is extremely convenient to use and demand for it will increase enormously in the next twenty years, probably surpassing that for any other type of fibre.

Synthetic rubbers

At present, synthetic rubbers represent about half the total amount of rubbers used, and their share of the world market will grow to at least 70–80 per cent. In fact, as far as we can tell, the increased demand for rubber will be almost entirely for the synthetic products. Within twenty years, the production of synthetic rubber will exceed 10 million tons per year, while that of natural rubber will remain almost constant.

Stereospecific polymerization processes have yielded products having the same chemical and steric constitution as natural rubber (cis-1, 4 polyisoprene), and gutta percha (trans-1, 4 polyisoprene), and having properties practically identical with those of the corresponding natural products, as well as new types of synthetic rubbers (for example, cis-1, 4 polybutadiene, having a high steric purity) made from less expensive starting materials. Moreover, the new processes give rubbers (ethylene-propylene copolymers and terpolymers) that are made from low-cost raw materials and have good elastic and dynamic properties – as well as a higher resistance to ageing than natural rubber because they are chemically more 'saturated' (less reactive).

Food production

The increased production of synthetic macromolecular products from coal and petroleum means that much of the land now used for the production of cotton, wood, natural rubber, etc., can be turned over to the growing of food. By this indirect means, macromolecular chemistry will help to feed the growing population of the world.

The problem of synthetic food is a new research topic in which investigations will be as important as for the other macromolecular substances I have discussed. However, the production of synthetic food raises remarkable difficulties. At first, we can expect only pure materials (for example, vitamins and some carbohydrates) to be produced by synthesis; meanwhile we must hope that the natural products will be produced in great amounts.

Computers

THE CUSTOMER'S IDEAL COMPUTER

by Lionel de Bournonville

Compagnie des Machines Bull, Paris

It is rather ticklish for an engineer specializing in electronic data-processing to make public his views on what the situation in this field will be in 1984. To do so properly, he must first keep his imagination, which may well be as fertile as that of the non-specialist, from running away with him and limit himself to what might logically be expected to happen. He must be honest in his foresight to avoid raising false hopes or being called 'dreamer' by his colleagues.

After twenty years of breathtaking advance in computation, there is at present no reason to be anything but optimistic about further improvements. Sooner or later we shall begin to get diminishing returns for our efforts, but so far, although we have encountered certain snags, there is no sign of falling off in the overall curve of computer progress.

Let us examine the prospects more closely. For the sake of clarity, I shall take a commercial viewpoint. A standard joke in the data-processing world concerns the qualities that customers expect from their machines: 'A do-it-all, instant machine which operates at no cost and requires no programming, not even an analysis of the problem.' How will machines tend towards this ideal?

(1) *The 'do-it-all' machine.* Frankly, the machines already do do quite a bit. By means of magnetic-tape electronic units with large-scale memories capable of retaining complex programmes, almost completely automated processing can be attained. These machines have such universal capabilities that the only thing holding them back at the present are questions of what data are valid and what rules they require for processing. Twenty years from now, a machine may be used to direct traffic for a large city,

provided that we have in the meanwhile discovered what data the machine would need and what mathematical, logical, and statistical processing laws are appropriate. It is certain that the trend will be towards machines that will process data as and where they are found. The aim is to do away with all go-betweens, especially transcriptions, which require burdensome human intervention. Certain advances have already been made in this vein, such as so-called 'real-time' machines, direct reading of documents, and so on. Their use will become more widespread with the use of inexpensive direct pick-up devices and the possible development of reliable machines that can read handwritten documents and interpret the human voice. But we had best stop here, lest we be accused of straying into the realm of science fiction.

Although large-capacity memories are available, we are bound to be dissatisfied with them in their present form as far as data-storage is concerned. Magnetic tape is a data medium of great linear density. But the 'access time' for retrieving the data is relatively long, and so far we have found nothing, of two or three dimensions, that gives comparable capacity at reasonable cost. Should data media of such density be found, with an access time in keeping with the speed of electronic processing, a great step forward will have been made towards the universality of machines. There is still, however, the possibility that the machine, faced with a mass of available data, may not be able to select the data appropriate to the problem being processed. In the human brain (a three-dimensional memory) access is random, but we are capable of choosing from among our memories only those having to do with a given situation. The machine should be able to make a similar choice without having to go through all the data stored within it. In short, the machine should function 'heuristically'.

(2) *The 'instant' machine.* Processing speed is a large factor in the ideal machine. Spectacular progress has been achieved in this respect over the last twenty years. Will speed continue to increase at the same rate? We find ourselves up against what is at present an insurmountable barrier – the speed of light, and hence the speed at which electrical impulses may be transmitted. We now deal in microseconds; light travels 300 metres in one micro-second. We are just beginning to speak of nanoseconds (10^{-9} second); light travels 30 cm in one nanosecond. To progress from

here, machines will have to be made smaller and divided into several specialized computers equipped for the parallel transmission of huge masses of data between themselves, and these data will have to be conveyed by something other than wires. Would this involve the use of light signals, and particularly the laser?

The speed of processing alone is not the whole of it; the speed with which information can be passed in and out of the machine may be a determining factor, too, and we have seen, in the case of the magnetic tape, how a balance, resulting in overall efficiency, was established. To be honest, nothing at present points categorically to a spectacular increase in input–output speeds in the near future. But who knows for certain? Take the example of printing speed: within the past twenty years printing speed has increased from 150 to 1,000 lines per minute. Will we attain 6,000 or 60,000 lines per minute, by substituting for our quasi-mechanical procedures some real electronic methods? This is an area where we are held back at present, but the future may rescue us.

(3) *The 'no-cost' machine*. Although we have seen the appearance of machines of ever-increasing performance, the prices have not risen in proportion. On the contrary, certain technical developments (such as magnetic tapes) tended to reduce the prices of machines of given performance. I think, however, that only by developing new techniques can we expect a really big reduction in price, until we finally arrive at computers that will be within the range of every pocket book. Will this point have been reached twenty years from now? That may be cutting it a bit short.

(4) *The 'easy to use' machine*. Granted, programming is a rather burdensome toll to pay for automatic data-processing. The efforts on the part of computer specialists to lighten this burden have been quite praiseworthy: symbolic and easy-to-handle machine languages, and the development of standard programming which does away with all work for certain processing phases. These programming aids are a first step, but by 1984 a customer wishing to have a problem processed may merely fill up a questionnaire and the machine will use his answers to compile its own optimum programme by assembling various pre-existing partial subroutines. It may be argued that, to deal with a wide variety of problems, the questionnaire would have to be long and detailed. So why not, instead, imagine specialized programming machines

which hold a conversation with the customer, taking into account the answers already given so that only useful questions are asked – and informing the customer, politely of course, of any contradictions in his answers? And here we are back in the field of science fiction, so we had better stop.

Our final note, however, is an optimistic one. We have no reason to fear a falling off in the development of data-processing equipment. 1984 may bring even greater wonders than are dreamed of in our philosophy.

THE BANISHMENT OF PAPER-WORK

by Dr Arthur L. Samuel

I.B.M. Thomas J. Watson Research Centre, Yorktown Heights, New York

It may come as a surprise to some to be told that the modern digital computer is really quite old in concept, and that the year 1984 will be celebrated as the 150th anniversary of the invention of the first computer, the Analytical Engine of the Englishman Charles Babbage. 150 years is really quite a long period of time in terms of modern science and industry and, at first glance, it seems unduly long for a new concept to come into full fruition. Unfortunately, Charles Babbage was ahead of his time, and it took 100 years of technical development, the impetus of the Second World War, and the perception of John Von Neumann to bring the computer into being. Now, twenty years later and with several generations of computers behind us, we are in a position to make a somewhat more meaningful prognosis than appeared possible in, say, 1948. We can only hope that we will not be as far off in actuality as we believe George Orwell to be, or as far off in our time scale as were Charles Babbage and his almost equally famous interpreter, Lady Lovelace.

Where, then, will the computer be in 1984? Computers are not going to get much bigger; in fact, they are going to get very much smaller, that is smaller in physical size, while retaining all of their presently envisioned computational capabilities. They will, of course, have access to very much bigger memories, memories which in fact can contain the total sum of man's recorded information – but this is already technically possible today. Nor are computers going to get much faster. They may be faster by a factor of 100 or even by 1,000, but not by anything like the factor of one million which has characterized the last twenty years' development. The finite velocity of light, and the discrete nature of matter and of energy, conspire to limit the attainable computational speed. Because of these limits the speed of our computers is not apt to change very much. We are learning a great deal about computer organization, and we can expect some startling changes along these lines, but these changes will be more apparent to the computer designer than to the user.

The large changes, and they will be large, will come in the way in which computers will be used and in the extent to which they will permeate the entire fabric of our society. Let us try to visualize these changes.

In the first place we have good reason for predicting that two rather basic problems will by then have been solved. The first of these has to do with learning, or rather its absence. At the present time, computers do not learn from their experience. Given a new problem to be solved, no matter how similar it may be to a previously solved problem, we, as humans, must write a new set of instructions, a programme in the jargon of the trade, to specify the solution procedure. Not only this, but unless we make special arrangements to save old information we frequently have to rewrite an identical set of instructions and even waste machine time by recomputing previously computed data. By contrast, when similar tasks are given to a human assistant, he is expected to learn from his experience; and a clerk who has failed to do so is likely to be looking for another position. This problem of machine learning should certainly have been solved well within the next twenty years, and the computer will then become a very much more useful device.

The second difficulty resides in the nature of the instructions which must now be given. The computer, today, accepts only imperative statements; it is a slave which executes our commands, and this without any ability to ask questions, volunteer information, discuss pros and cons with respect to solution methods, etc. In short, one cannot converse with a computer. Here, too, we can confidently look to a practical solution within a period short compared with twenty years.

Meanwhile, as a result of these two difficulties, we now find it necessary to employ a veritable army of people called 'programmers' to write instructions for the computer. When these problems have been solved, programming as we now know it will have ceased to exist and the computer will then be a truly 'intelligent' and reliable assistant.

A third current difficulty of a less basic sort will also have been solved within the next few years. It concerns the construction of simple input and output equipment for both oral and visual communication with the computer. This is already largely a problem of cost and, with time, we can expect to have extremely cheap and convenient terminals which will also be highly portable. Communication with a computer will then be easy and natural – as easy and natural as communication with an intelligent servant of the human variety.

Given computers that are perhaps 100 to 1,000 times as fast as the fastest present-day computers, computers with larger memories, computers which occupy perhaps one one hundredth the volume that they now do, computers that are much cheaper, and, finally, computers which learn from their experience and which can converse freely with their masters – what can we predict?

To be completely realistic, we must postulate two quite different situations, the one in which nearly everyone has his own private computer, and the second situation in which the private ownership of computers is banned by law, but in which each person has access to a small terminal connecting him with one or more large state-owned computers giving him most of the advantages of a small privately-owned computer, but without the opportunity for private or, perhaps some would say, clandestine operations. Capitalist countries will tend in the first direction while communist states will doubtlessly go in the second direction although even in these countries the 'big brother is watching' aspect will be very much less pronounced than was predicted in 1948. Lest we of the West view this dichotomy with complacency, one must note that a trend towards the large central installation is also evident in the western world. One might, therefore, expect that an intermediate situation will develop in the West with private ownership of computers of limited capabilities which also serve as remote terminals to communicate with the centrally located computers for the solution of larger problems. Computers will in any case be as convenient to use and as readily available as the present day telephone.

Telephones will, of course, be portable and connected via radio so that one need not be at any special location to obtain phone communication only with one's computer. Tele-video-phones via radio will be well developed although not yet in widespread use, and the terminals will still be rather bulky, so that one may still have to go to fixed locations if one wishes video-communication with a computer.

Connexion to a central location will be very necessary to perform another function which will, by then, be delegated to the omnipresent computer. I refer to information retrieval. The entire contents of the large central files (or at least that portion which the government elects to make available) will be readily retrievable by anyone at a moment's notice. One will be able to browse through the fiction section of the central library, enjoy an evening's light entertainment viewing any movie that has ever been produced (for a suitable fee, of course, since Hollywood will still be commercial), or inquire as to the previous day's production figures for tin in Bolivia – all for the asking via one's remote terminal. Libraries for books will have ceased to exist in the more advanced countries except for a few which will be preserved at museums, and most of the world's knowledge will be in machine-readable form. Perhaps it would be more correct to say, all of the world's recorded knowledge will be in this form since the art of programming computers to read printed and handwritten material will have been fully developed. However, the storage problem will make it imperative that a more condensed form of recording be used, a form which will only be machine-readable, and which will be translated into human-readable form by one's computer on demand.

The consequences of this compilation and ready access to large amounts of stored information will be truly profound in many diverse fields, such for example as agronomy, jurisprudence, and medicine, to name but three. But all this is another subject.

Computers will perform yet another major function – that of language translation. Not only will one be able to obtain information from the central files in the language of one's choice, but automatic translation via the telephone will also have come into use – although perhaps not general use, because of the cost and because of the gradual drift towards a universal language. It will, nevertheless, be possible to dial anywhere in the world and to converse with anyone speaking a different language with only a slight translation delay to allow for the differences in sentence structure and word-ordering between the languages.

Perhaps we should say something about teaching machines, which will have been developed to such an extent that master-computers of large capacity will be needed, each to direct many slave-teaching machines and to compile data from them. These master-computers will alter teaching methods on the basis of experience. They will up-date the material and its ideological slant as dictated by scientific advances and the changing *mores* of society. While it will be entirely feasible to obtain an education at home, via one's own personal computer, human nature will not have changed, and there will still be a need for schools with laboratories, classrooms, and individual teachers to motivate the students.

So far, we have talked primarily about the individual user and his personal use of the computer. But the digital computer is destined to play an even bigger role in the real-time control of projects and processes. The coordination and scheduling of any large endeavour, whether it be running a business, operating a factory, constructing a large building or running a government, now takes a fantastic amount of paper-work. This paper-work will cease to exist in twenty years. Instead, direct inputs and out-puts to the computer will provide information, initiate the necessary processes (all computer controlled by a lesser breed of computers), and finally issue what few instructions are needed for the few people who are still involved.

Process control with the attending automation, while delegated to simpler computers, will have reached a very high degree of development so that the number of factory employees will drop precipitously. These displaced people will be going into the service industries, and a few into the design and maintenance of the machines which replace them. Science and the arts will be flourishing. The working week will have been shortened to four days, but we shall have an unemployment problem. Making this due prediction will, of course, help to nullify it. Many people (including the author and his associates) are taking steps to make the transition to automated production an orderly one without socially undesirable side-effects.

Finally, a word regarding solid intellectual achievements of computers. The world draughts, chess, and go champions will, of course, have met defeat at the hands of the computer, but strangely enough this will not have ended these three games either as intellectual pastimes or as professional career activities. It is true that matches between people will be less common, but nearly everyone will know his precise rating as a player and he will endeavour to improve his ability by playing against his computer. Computers will have largely taken over the task of composing and arranging music, at least for popular entertainment, and many people will vie with each other in regard to the quality of mood music which their own personal computer or personal programme can produce. As far as literature is concerned, the computer will still be a neophyte although 'who-done-its' will be turned out by the million. Computers will not have contributed as much as some people have predicted, with respect to making basic contributions to mathematics and science and, somehow or other, all attempts to invest them with truly creative abilities will have failed.

There will still be a place in the world for people!

A WORLD DOMINATED BY COMPUTERS?

by Dr M. V. Wilkes, F.R.S.

University Mathematical Laboratory, Cambridge

Twenty years on takes us to 1984; twenty years back takes us to 1944, which happens to be the year in which the first digital computer ever built started working at Harvard University and which may, therefore, be taken as the beginning of the computer age. The foundations were well laid, and people were soon designing computers that were truly universal. The power of computers has increased because they have come to be faster and to have more storage capacity, and because better programming techniques have been evolved. This is how advances will continue, rather than by the invention of wholly new kinds of computer.

Much of the progress of the last few years has stemmed from the introduction of techniques whereby a computer can share its time between a number of tasks. Until fairly recently, these new techniques were welcomed primarily because they enabled machines to be used more efficiently; now their potential in enabling a lot of users to use the same computer simultaneously is beginning to be realized. Very soon the computer will become a public utility. We shall see everywhere in shops and offices, laboratories and factories, keyboards looking very like typewriters, but connected to a computer. In addition there will be graphical display devices on which diagrams may be drawn either by the user or by the computer itself. The computer will have a very large store and one of its primary functions will be to act as a ' data base', that is to hold files of information, some public, some private.

Soon computers in different areas will be talking to each other so that any user can interrogate any file available to any of the computers. For example, a draughtsman might want to inspect a drawing produced the day before in a remote part of the organization in which he works.

Once a network of computers exists – and by 1984 it will be an international network – it will be the obvious thing to use computers for the transmission of messages. Many messages, especially those in plain language, have much unnecessary redundancy in them, and the computer at the sending end will first compress the message by removing this redundancy. It will then systematically add fresh redundancy for use in controlling the accuracy of transmission. The computer at the distant end will restore the message to its original form after making sure that it has been accurately received. The saving in the cost of long-distance transmission resulting from the compression of the message will easily pay for the cost of the computer time.

Speech will also be transmitted as data and reconstituted at the far end. When you talk to a business associate in the United States and would just as soon have your English accent suppressed (along with any emotion that might creep into your voice and give away your business secrets) then you will save money by asking for the maximum compression possible, and will allow the computer at the far end to speak with its own accent. If, on the other hand,

you are ringing up your loved one in a distant country you will
order less compression and pay the bill gladly.

We read in science fiction of computers acquiring superhuman
reasoning powers and beginning to exert a tyranny over men. I
do not have any fear of this happening, and certainly not by 1984.
It would mean a breakthrough in the direction of programming
computers so that they can learn, and this would, it seems to me,
be such a stupendous breakthrough that it is unlikely to happen for
a very long time. There is interesting work going on in artificial
intelligence, but the term is misleading and what is really being
studied is new ways of programming computers to solve
problems.

Although machines are not to be feared in themselves, they
will make it possible for those in authority to keep much closer
tabs on what people are doing, and there are signs that governments are beginning to realize this. The United States Internal
Revenue is installing a very large computer system, and it will
soon be extremely difficult for any American to avoid paying his
full income tax, since, whenever he makes a financial transaction
that is likely to attract tax, information about it will be fed into the
system. This is perhaps all right, but how would you feel if you
had exceeded the speed limit on a deserted road in the dead of
night, and a few days later received a demand for a fine that had
been automatically printed by a computer coupled to a radar
system and vehicle-identification device ? It might not be a
demand at all, but simply a statement that your bank account
had been debited automatically. Many branches of life will
lend themselves to continuous computer surveillance, and I
leave it to the readers to decide whether or not this is a
pleasant prospect.

One of the few really new research techniques that computers
have made possible is computer simulation. This has already
yielded important results, especially in situations in which
ordinary theoretical analysis is difficult or impossible. It can also
be used as an alternative to performing experiments, when these
are difficult or costly. By 1984 it will be in regular use for economic policy-making. It will, perhaps, make possible one of the
next steps in the present spectacular advance being made in bio-
physics. As soon as people begin to think that they understand

sufficiently well the mechanism of genetic codes, protein synthesis, and the rest, then it should be possible to programme a simulation on a sufficiently large computer and see how it works out. One would aim to start with a simple system and see if conditions can be found in which the complexity builds up in a systematic manner, and in which something like physiological reproduction and growth takes place. Work of this kind may well have made some progress by 1984.

Telecommunications

PRIVATE TELEVISION INSTEAD OF TRAVEL

by Dr J. R. Pierce

Bell Telephone Laboratories, Murray Hill, New Jersey

It is very difficult to guess how telecommunications may have advanced by 1984, because new discoveries and inventions continually open up new possibilities and opportunities, so that the world becomes neither a logical development of the present, as some novelists and scholars portray it, nor a fanciful dream contradicting known science, as others would have it. But, whatever telecommunications may be like in 1984, they will contain in them vestiges of a past, which is our present, and it is to the possible nature of these vestiges that I propose to address myself.

One aspect of the present is growth in a broad field of data transmission. This includes teletypewriter, which is now more popular in Europe than in America; the transmission of scientific and business information from computer to computer and from office to office; the operation of computerized airline reservation services involving terminals in many cities and, by 1984, in many countries.

I am sure that there will be a great growth in the use of, and needs for, such communication by 1984. I expect that office typewriters will routinely reduce messages to machine-readable form, and will also type them out from such recordings. I expect that most of the sort of business letters which are now sent by airmail, and perhaps most business correspondence, will be sent electrically from such machine-readable records. Further, there will be an increase in uses of digital transmission, and probably its extension into the home for making theatre, hotel, and travel reservations, and for shopping.

Digital transmission is sure to grow because the initial demands for channel capacity are within the capabilities of the existing international network of telephone transmission, which now efficiently links those countries having the greatest need for inter-communication, and will soon link more effectively more and more of the countries of the world.

While overland cable, coaxial cable, and microwave facilities, together with undersea submarine telephone cables, are adequate for its initial growth, data transmission is already having an impact on transmission means. Thus, already in my country there is a growing use of pulsed, digital, on–off, binary transmission systems for sending either telephone signals in a coded form (pulse code modulation), or data signals via cables. By 1984, such digital trans-mission systems will have interconnected most parts of the more advanced countries, and probably will have extended overseas.

Digital transmission systems will not only make it possible to transmit more data and to transmit data faster; they will make something else economically feasible. That is, the encryption for privacy or secrecy of telephone and, eventually, of television transmission. Such private or secret transmission is bound to play an increasingly important part in both government and business affairs.

At present, the dispersal of the world's population, together with air travel, puts an almost intolerable burden on man. He shuttles across continents and oceans for a few hours or even for a few minutes of private conversation.

Will telecommunications largely take the place of travel by 1984? If this is to be so, we must assure some degree of secrecy. And, we must have more communication – more perhaps in the sense of television with conferences – and cheaper communica-tion. Here we outstrip our present resources in communication systems. But among three things we may find relief.

One is transmission of very broad bands of frequencies through pipes or 'waveguides' by means of millimetre waves having frequencies from 50,000 to 100,000 millions of cycles per second. This range of frequencies is about five times as great as the whole range of so-called microwave frequencies which are commonly used in microwave radio relay and radar, and about twenty times as great as the range of microwave frequencies assigned to common-carrier communication. And, the same frequencies can be used over and over again, side by side, in closed waveguides.

Through decades of research, a sound technical base has been laid for millimetre-wave waveguides. Whether they will come into use depends on the rate at which a need for more channel capacity develops and whether some other means of communication forestalls their development.

Communication by means of coherent light beams, generated by lasers and guided by lenses, reflectors, or other means through buried tubes, might outstrip millimetre-wave waveguides and provide the broad-band overland circuits of 1984. Today, it is too early to tell. Many problems are still either unsolved or undisclosed.

Finally, in spanning oceans, and perhaps in spanning continents, communication satellites will provide an important part of our communication channels by 1984.

In the near future, to establish any sort of economical satellite communication system will require the very best of the world's technical resources. It will require great financial resources as well, for great risks are involved. Once satellite communication is established as a technically and financially successful part of international communication, however, technological progress will be rapid, and we should expect revolutionary changes and developments between the first practical system and satellite communication of 1984.

Thus, as vestiges of the past, I see by 1984 greatly extended data communication and improved telecommunications as a substitute for travel. On the technical side, both of these will involve great advances in means of transmission, including the inauguration of commercially successful satellite communication systems.

But 1984 may be dominated by other vestiges of the past. Ours is a time of increasing nationalism, a time in which a nation's scientific and technological resources and manpower are coming to be viewed increasingly as a valuable property and asset of the government in establishing and maintaining its international political position. This may so displace and hamper the old non-political internationalism of telecommunications science and technology as to seriously delay the development, say, of satellite communication systems. On the other hand, new discoveries and inventions could sweep away many of the vestiges of the past which I have assumed to persist into 1984.

DECENTRALIZATION BY TELECOMMUNICATIONS

by J. D. Clare

Standard Telecommunication Laboratories, Harlow

The choice of the new telecommunications facilities to be made available during the next twenty years is likely to depend more on the demands of society than on the skills of the manufacturers. That this has always been true to some extent is illustrated by the innovation of the telephone which, after introduction to the director's desk as a status symbol, later became one of the accepted housekeeping aids of the suburban housewife.

Any extension of good-quality communication systems is associated with a spiralling increase of demand, which rapidly makes use of the increase in utility. Typically, this is illustrated by the unexpected rapidity with which the first transatlantic submarine telephone cable was filled with traffic. It would appear that the latent need for people to be able to communicate directly over any distance has not been adequately assessed or satisfied and that any method used to predict future requirements in the telecommunications industry, which is based solely on the extrapolation of growth curves, might well prove unsound if it is extended to 1984.

This uncertainty is further enhanced by the very rapid advance of scientific discoveries and technical capability and the decreasing time-scale necessary to develop them. Though less obvious to the engineers and scientists specializing in the technologies associated with telecommunications, social structures are also subject to a similarly increasing rate of change.

Many factors are involved – car production, transport, living standards, building methods, and population growth are but a few – and the British government's Buchanan report on traffic in towns was concerned with a detailed examination of some of these influences. Accepting the grave problems associated with personal transport, which were highlighted in the report, it is reasonable to deduce that considerable amelioration could be obtained if there were far greater emphasis on decentralization of population and industry which can be effective only with vastly improved telecommunications.

In any event, traffic networks of the future will need special control systems based on automatic observation techniques and, associated with these, there must be adequate communication facilities to feed information to and from the control centres.

The effects of automation must also be considered. It is, perhaps, in the 'process industries' that future trends are most apparent, though the word automation is less often used there. A product such as mineral gas can be controlled automatically from the raw material in the ground to the supply to the general public. With the additional provision of computer-controlled accountancy and billing through a bank, the organization's staff requirement could be almost entirely limited to maintenance employees. If automation to this degree were to spread to any extent, the relationship existing at present between industry and population would be significantly changed. If one of the main restrictions determining population distribution is thus removed, decentralization could be achieved more reasonably.

The resulting demands for a more sophisticated telecommunications network must lead to the provision of many new services. In order to remove the need for the majority of the personal contacts at present necessary in most business operations and to provide facilities that obviate gatherings at conferences, telecommunications must provide a form of high-definition colour television associated with high quality audio channels – every blush and nuance needs to be accurately conveyed. Looking into the even more remote future, it may not be too fanciful to imagine that other senses will be simulated remotely.

The technical problems of transmission of sight and sound, and the design of the appropriate transducers, are soluble with presently known techniques, although developments within the next twenty years should make them economically much more attractive. However, a major problem lies in associating camera movements with the behaviour of a speaker. The effect of being addressed from a TV receiver by an individual who is apparently looking away from one is most disconcerting, and must be 'designed out' to achieve a suitable system. The simulated conference presented on television presently requires an army of technicians with full studio facilities so that the receiver may see a performer looking him straight in the eye at one moment and catch a glimpse of a discomfited fellow performer at the next. Experiments in which eyeball movements have been tracked to operate following servo systems may well be a key to the solution of this problem.

The wide band characteristics of the transmission network needed to handle these 'face to face' communications would facilitate the application of digital encryption to confidential matter, whether in the form of speech, video, or facsimile. The same network would also be well suited to handling the transmission of text within a decentralized organization. A system could be provided that would make material available on the typewriter of the addressee at the start of the working day, thus eliminating today's problems associated with envelopes, franking, sorting, registration, and office delivery. Similarly, remote access to data-retrieval systems could be envisaged which would supply reference data on demand, either as hard copy or ephemerally on a cathode ray tube. Both internal and public data-retrieval systems would be required. These possibilities are also referred to in the articles on computers (p. 139).

The communication services available in the home will inevitably be increased as a result of the services provided for industry. Considering the manner in which the telephone was introduced to the community, it may well be that the combination of a vision channel with the telephone will spread in a similar manner. The introduction of optical–electrical transducers associated with the communication network could make possible such activities as the remote reading of supply meters, and the presentation of bank statements via a data link. The direct debiting of bank accounts by shops, on the operation of a credit-card transaction, may make the latter service vital.

If the new facilities suggested were provided and linked to active planning for decentralization of industry and population, then this arrangement could well provide a more acceptable solution to some of the problems of the future than such proposals as the rebuilding of our city centres suggested in the Buchanan report. If these possible demands for new facilities are linked with the latent need for people to communicate with each other, which so far has by no means been satisfied, then by 1984 we should see a vast extension of the telecommunications network coupled with a significant change in the concept of its place in modern society.

MASS COMMUNICATIONS IN 1984

by Sir Gerald Barry

Granada TV Network

What particular kinds and shapes of telecommunications *apparatus* will be in general use in the 1980s it is for the technologists to predict. Among so many possible variants a good deal is likely to depend on chance – on which manufacturer succeeds first with what, and so sets the accepted patterns. Already, the wrist-watch radio powered by body-heat, the handbag colour TV set, the home set built into the wall of every room or carried from room to room and hung up like a picture-frame, have become common currency of gossip for the next decade: possible variations or developments seem almost limitless. But from what we know of what Lord Todd calls the 'seeds' already sown, certain broad predictions about the future nature of telecommunications are clearly valid.

To start at the beginning, it seems certain that twenty years from now there will have been accomplished a technical revolution in both the printing and the distribution of news comparable to the revolution caused by the invention of printing itself. A newspaper distributed by van or pushed through the letter-box will have become a preposterous anachronism. With the introduction of photo-composition replacing 'raised' type, and with the simultaneous typesetting and printing of several editions of a single newspaper thousands of miles apart, the cumbrous old-world methods of newspaper production are already fast on their way out. Indeed, but for the millions of capital invested in obsolescent machinery and for deep-rooted trade union customs, the overdue shake-up in the newspaper industry would have begun much sooner. Web-offset and gravure methods of printing have set off changes in newspaper technique that are about to affect radically the whole newspaper economy: and since they lend themselves best (at present at least) to local and regional publications, they may occasion a vigorous come-back for local journalism and a healthy check on monopoly.

So much for the short run. What of the longer-term prospects? What exact effect these and other more drastic changes may ultimately exert on the future of the printed word one cannot yet foresee; but in the area of mass-communication it is predictable that, in the long-term, the 'newspaper' of the future will be electronic – if, indeed, it can be called a newspaper in the presently accepted sense at all. People will probably get their news either on a television screen or on a wall panel or on a private teleprinter, or on some variant or combination of these devices. It may come through a subscription service to Pay-TV. The 'reader' may dial a number and receive 'page 1', holding it as long as he needs and changing back and forth from page to page at his whim – or dialling last week's paper or last year's, or reading the *New York Times* while sitting in Clapham SW. A bookish subscriber may be able at will to check a quotation from *Coriolanus* or a footnote in Chapter XLVII of Gibbon.

But by 1984 one foresees that the mainstream of journalism, as covered by what are now the popular newspapers and probably directly affecting the serious ones too, will have passed firmly into the hands of television itself. Nothing can match the actuality of event-plus-person summoned instantaneously together before the eye – there in the living-room, though they may happen at the time to be on the moon. There is, after all, nothing sacrosanct about a news*paper* as such: if a full and free flow of news, comment, and criticism can be more conveniently and attractively supplied by television, then the needs of democracy will be served (though this is itself, of course, to beg an enormous question).

By 1984, transmission on several channels, in colour, may well be continuous round the daylight clock. Parliament will be televised in one form or another. Most of the political restrictions now imposed on television but not on newspapers will be abolished (the breakthrough has already begun). Via Eurovision and the communications satellites and possibly newer contrivances, instantaneous reporting will be available at the bedside from any corner of the globe, and perhaps beyond.

In television, the other major predictable development will have occurred in the field of education. For schools, but more especially for further education, and by means of closed-circuit in the universities, television will have become accepted as an everyday adjunct of instruction. Within a couple of decades at most I foresee a breakthrough from the system which, since the middle ages, has confined a don to one individual campus. There will be *inter*-university lectures and courses; as well as innumerable correspondence courses for extra-mural students conducted by television.

What sort of world will all this help to create? Just as the air-craft revolutionized strategy, diplomacy, and commerce by replacing the slow-boat and the carrier-pigeon with face-to-face confrontations for statesmen and businessmen, so telecommunications may reverse the process and permit Prime Ministers and tycoons again to remain chair-borne. Although M. Satre ('Travelling by air in 1984', page 169) reminds us that super-sonic flight will bring the Antipodes within a mere seven hours of London, the simple device of telephone-plus-television will often make the fastest journey seem unnecessary. It will be instructive to discover the extent to which, among the 'top people' of 1984, actual physical presence is still considered an advantage. As for travelling for pleasure or leisure, we may assume that genuine tastes, smells, and sunshine will still retain an edge over the allure-ments of stereoscopic colour on the screen.

It seems possible that the resources of total visual communication about to come into being may occasion social changes in the areas of knowledge and understanding as radical as those brought about by the invention of printing itself. The opportunities look to be immense. Properly used, they could hasten forward by decades the acceptance of One World, by familiarizing to the peoples of all nations the differing ideas and attitudes of Western, Eastern, and African man, not only in politics but over the whole spectrum of human life. Similarly, a seriously directed 'journal-ism' could interest and prepare people – in a world in which, as we have been warned, a technological 'explosion' is imminent – for the immense and relatively sudden industrial and social developments they will have to accept, could atune their minds and emotions to change, and so minimize the frictions and inadequacies that today delay and frustrate progress.

There is another direction in which it seems possible a valuable social benefit might emerge. Just as what may be called the 'public storage' of computer information can be made virtually limitless, so, by the last two decades of this century, perhaps much sooner, 'private storage' may similarly have become regular domestic practice. The family video-tape recording machine is already almost with us, and with it and its heirs and successors will be brought within the reach of thousands the means to make and share their own programmes locally or within individual groups. The local 'station' and the equivalent of the local theatre may flourish. Here one may legitimately foresee a possible development of some promise for a more indigenous and creative community life, a challenging corrective to the canned entertainment and mass persuasion that make us all the passive victims of output from a central pumping-station.

On the one hand there will exist, with the universal provision of do-it-yourself electronic equipment, the means to encourage locally and regionally a more vigorous cultural and political life; on the other hand, the virtually limitless powers of centralized supply will pull in the opposite direction. Again, it will be instructive to note which tendency prevails: on the outcome may depend a great deal for the happiness and fulfilment of the coming generations. One can foresee at least the requisites for a movement that might revitalize urban communities.

And here, after all, in all these absorbing exercises in crystal-gazing, rests the only thing that matters: man itself. It is enlivening to speculate on the means that will soon be at his disposal: what matters is the uses he will choose to put them to. We must assume a society brought up under Robbins and Newsom, housed (or just beginning to be) under Buchanan, having at its command an unimaginable array of electronic gadgetry, and invigorating new avenues of health and leisure. To what ends will they be put? What sort of world, what kind of life, are they going to want, this next-generation-but-one? This is something no computer can tell us: and I for one would petition the professors of geriatrics to hasten forward with their labours so that I might survive to see for myself.

Aviation

MARKET NEEDS AND TECHNICAL POSSIBILITIES

by Dr M. J. Lighthill, F.R.S.

Formerly Director, Royal Aircraft Establishment, Farnborough

Two separate streams of development generate, by their imperfect interaction, the changing pattern of aviation. One is the development of market needs, whether for military or civil aircraft. The other is the development of technical possibilities, whether for engines, airframes, or aircraft equipment.

To forecast the pattern of aviation in 1984, it is necessary to survey the conceivable patterns of development of market needs (as influenced by likely technical innovations) and judge which is most probable, and also to survey the conceivable patterns of development of technical possibilities (as influenced by likely market requirements) and judge which of them is most probable and, finally, to forecast the most likely result of the interaction of the market needs and the technical possibilities.

Market needs: military

The military requirements, which hitherto have represented the greatest part of the market for aviation products, are the part hardest to forecast twenty years ahead. Futures that are, no doubt, possible include total disarmament and, as the opposite extreme, devotion by the most highly developed nations of an increasing proportion of their increasing productive capacity to preparation for wars of every conceivable scale and duration.

Like many others, I am inclined to reject these extreme hypotheses. Concord among the nations may, as we fervently hope, reach the stage when peaceful machinery for settling cases where powerful interests are in conflict becomes accepted. It is unlikely, however, that those powerful interests could tolerate a situation in which irresponsible local disputes might develop unchecked into war. On the most optimistic view that appears tenable, armed forces would be needed, able to deploy substantial force at very short notice to any trouble spot. One may speculate whether such forces should in normal conditions be concentrated (for efficient training), dispersed (for maximum deterrence), or both, but probably in all cases they would need to be capable of rapid long-range reinforcement. This role, with others such as reconnaissance and strike, would be expected to make continued demands for efficient air power. Manned interceptors might also be necessary to interrogate suspicious aircraft, since lawbreakers could easily acquire dangerous offensive strength by converting civil aircraft.

Alternatively, law and order in 1984 may be maintained, not by one mobile, flexible, and efficient world force, but by the continued balance of opposing forces. However, one may expect the nature of such a balance to be increasingly changed by the fact that a very few groups can convince other groups of their ability to cause more destruction, in those other groups' homelands, in the first few hours of a conflict, than in all previous wars put together, independently of any destructive action by the other side. The chances that a nation may seek to develop defensive or pre-emptive forces capable of invalidating a second-strike threat against it are likely to recede, owing to the crippling increases in the cost of such a system that appear achievable by relatively cheap increases in the degree of sophistication of the second-strike threat itself.

The greatest nations may then be able greatly to slow down the development of new strategic retaliatory forces. On the other hand, their interest in being able to limit local conflicts drastically, in respect of intensity, area and duration, will increase. They, or alliances of which they form part, are likely to need highly mobile, versatile and effective forces for use in limited war. Indeed, the only qualitative difference from the type of force discussed under the previous hypothesis would lie in the need to be effective in the possible presence of well-equipped opposition.

To sum up, the market needs for military aircraft in 1984 may be dominated by the need for highly mobile forces able quickly to bring under control an explosive situation anywhere in the world. Effective transport, not too dependent on facilities at the destination point, with reconnaissance, strike and interception, must be provided. Serious doubt remains, however, on how well equipped a defence such a force should be organized to cope with.

Market needs: civil

The civil requirement for aircraft has grown fast since the Second World War. Few people doubt that it will continue to grow, but the rate of increase is not easy to predict. The number of passenger-miles flown on scheduled flights increased about 4-fold in the decade between 1950 and 1960. Rising standards of living, reductions by about 30 per cent in the average fare paid (relative to the general price level), and increasing spread of 'international awareness' are guessed to have contributed to this. Most people guess that similar factors will operate in the next two decades, but with somewhat less total effect; possibly a 2-fold increase between 1964 and 1974 might be followed by a further $1\frac{1}{2}$-fold increase by 1984. But the precise rate of increase is believed to be highly sensitive to such fare reductions as may be offered, so that one of the most important requirements for new airline types will be economy of operation.

Apart from the appeal of air travel to individuals, great political and commercial interests benefit very substantially from a system that makes all parts of the world rapidly accessible and, partly for this reason, governments commonly assist civil aviation, although giving it every possible inducement to pay its own way.

Governments, furthermore, in many countries, have been most effective, through regulation, research, and education, in promoting safety in civil aircraft operations. The present average fatal accident rate on scheduled services, of 1 per 100 million passenger-miles, means that on the average an individual may expect to pay about £3 million in fares before meeting with a fatal accident. The process of further reducing the risk to crew and passengers must, however, continue.

It is sometimes imagined that speed is the enemy of economy and safety, and that airlines are forced to higher-speed aircraft only on the basis of their undoubted passenger appeal. Hitherto, however, economy and safety have actually improved with increase of speed (which increases the miles flown per aircraft per annum). Supersonic airliners are, from the start, being designed around the existing standards of economy and safety. In addition, it is expected that experience with their production and operation will show how the increased seat-mile productivity which supersonic speed permits and the perfection of new safety techniques such as automatic landing will, ultimately, allow both to be improved upon. The design of these and other new civil aircraft is limited by one other main consideration, namely, that annoyance caused on the ground by their emitted sound cannot be allowed to rise above somewhere about its present level.

The civil market includes the use of aircraft for freight, agricultural, and survey purposes, which can also be expected to grow very fast indeed in the next twenty years. Economic and safety considerations will again dominate the rate of future expansion; but there are already many parts of the world where aerial seeding, top-dressing, and pest control, in particular, have shown a very handsome profit, in spite of difficult safety considerations.

Technological possibilities

From what has been said, the difficulty of forecasting with any precision the requirements for aircraft coming into service in 1984 must be evident. But, even if second sight allowed this, it would still be impossible to pinpoint the developments, aimed at meeting those requirements, that are most likely to attract adequate capital support in the 1970s. Among many reasons for this, an important one is the certainty that another ten years of accumulation of new knowledge in a technology where the pace of research is hot will cause big changes in the balance of expected advantage between one development and another.

One must, then, recognize many more technological possibilities for future development than will ever come to fruition. In the selection of those that I shall mention, I may appear to be taking out and redusting certain ideas of respectable antiquity. For example, on laminar flow much work was in progress already during the Second World War. In many of these cases, however, one should speak not of antiquity but of maturity. A good idea in aeronautics constantly evolves, as more and more essential engineering detail is elucidated and what the idea can achieve is becoming more precisely known. At the same time, those achievements have to be matched to constantly changing needs, and the new balance between potential and need has constantly to be reviewed.

Of course, an idea continues to mature long after first flight, and the very best ideas in aeronautics have exhibited astounding resilience and vitality. For example, the classical straight-wing-tail-fuselage combination showed almost endless capacity for development and continues to be selected against requirements for runway-based aircraft operating over short stage-lengths. A later configurational idea, the use of swept wings with careful fuselage and wing shapings near the kink in the lifting surface, is already of respectable antiquity but promises well, as we shall see, for further development.

Similarly, no doubt, newer aerodynamic ideas, like the sharp-edged slender delta of the Concorde or, beyond that, what we may call the 'lifting propulsive duct', have extended futures ahead of them, and any such idea may be combined, as time goes on, with many different motifs in the structural, propulsive, and systems fields.

Laminar flow

The drag of an aircraft arises from energy fed by it into the air through which it flies. One part of this energy goes into creating the downward air movement (a double vortex) necessary to give the aircraft lift, but another part goes into the useless wake, by friction between the aircraft surface and the air near it. Under normal conditions, the thin shearing layer where the frictional forces act does not have airspeed distributed across it in a laminated manner, because that flow condition is unstable; instead, the layer breaks up into turbulent eddies, which transfer much more energy to the surrounding air than simple viscous action would do. Over twenty years' work has demonstrated that, by sucking part of this layer through either a porous or a slotted wing surface, what remains can be rendered stable, partly because it is so thin and partly because the distribution of airspeed across it is conducive to laminar flow.

Experiments in flight continue, and difficulties remain to be overcome, but it must be regarded as a serious possibility that an important increase in payload or range may have been obtained by these means in some aircraft for civil or military purposes or both by 1984.

All-wing aircraft

The possibility of all-wing designs for transport applications, to make the whole structure bear the lift to balance its weight, with the aim of reducing the loads to be transmitted through it, has often been studied. Many difficulties arise, but techniques for overcoming most of them are under development.

Combination of this idea with laminar flow has its attractions, since 'laminarization' of fuselages is difficult. Looking far into the future, one may suppose that beyond the first generation supersonic airliner, which is already half-way towards being an all-lifting surface, the next step might be laminarization (which could in principle improve supersonic economics even more than subsonic) in combination with an all-wing design.

Without laminarization, the all-wing concept shows some promise also for economic short-range operation – a specialized role in which the main difficulty of compact all-wing designs, namely, a reduced lift-drag ratio at low speeds, is of reduced importance.

Variable sweepback

This application of the swept-wing idea has also had to wait a long time before engineering practicability and market demands were matched, in the American TFX project. This is designed to meet a military requirement in which the emphasis is on flexibility, that is, in appropriateness to more than one service, to the strike and interception roles, etc. An important feature of the aircraft will be low fuel consumption during loiter in the straight-wing condition and high supersonic dash capability in the swept-wing condition.

What can be expected of second-generation variable sweep aircraft ? Present researches offer at least the hope of wing shaping yielding really high lift-drag efficiencies at two quite different 'cruising' speeds, subsonic and high-supersonic; this might have several applications. At the same time, the permanence of the 'hinge' method of varying sweep is not certain. In theory an all-wing shape might be designed, that could be flown as a straight wing at low speeds and 'slewed' round as a whole by up to 70° to the direction of flight at high speeds to reduce drag. Improvements in automatic control techniques might render asymmetrical flying of this kind possible in the future.

Speed

One idea, of, indeed, more respectable antiquity than any, is that aircraft speeds can with benefit be increased. A 'barrier' to further speed increase has from time to time been alleged; but past barriers were successively broken by the evolution of the clean-aircraft concept (sometimes called 'streamlining'), the development of the gas turbine, and the abandonment of straight wings – in each case with an improvement in operational economy. The present barrier to practical use of higher speeds than 'Mach 2 plus', namely, the 'heat barrier', is almost certain to be similarly penetrated in the years ahead.

In the meantime, it has been circuitously circumvented by the development of spacecraft, lifted out of the atmosphere by rockets before acceleration to speeds ten times more than 'Mach 2 plus'. They avoid the atmospheric-heating barrier, but the speeds needed to remain in orbit are inconveniently high for many practical applications.

The question arises, therefore, whether, in addition to this 'revolutionary' approach to increase in speed, there exists the possibility of an 'evolutionary' approach, beginning say with aircraft capable of speeds up to Mach 5 and heights up to 125,000 ft, aimed at appropriate market needs. New shapes which appear likely to be suitable for such aircraft include 'wave riding' shapes which 'ride' a shock wave in the manner of a planing hydrofoil, and in which propulsive and lifting systems are no longer of a different order of size and therefore have to be designed as a single whole. They may augment lift at the highest altitudes by jet deflection. The airframe structure may use materials hitherto reserved for the hot end of jet engines; the engine itself, and the cabin, will need elaborate cooling systems giving up heat to unburned fuel and probably also to water. A particularly difficult feature will be the matching of aerodynamics and propulsion to the low-speed as well as to the high-speed flight regime; variable geometry will again be needed, possibly in the lifting surfaces, but certainly in the engine installation.

Vertical take-off

The pioneering of vertical take-off in the U.K. seems likely to be followed by worldwide adoption in a variety of roles. The immediate improvements that can be foreseen include development of instrumented landing and take-off to permit economic operation under all conditions with minimum (and, where necessary, zero) site preparation.

In those military applications, at which current orders for VTOL aircraft are aimed, it may in addition become more and more desirable to be able to use any relatively flat area that may be available to increase payload or range (or both) above their values for pure vertical take-off. The evolution of designs with favourable 'ground effect' (the principle used in hovercraft) might help here. If the lift on a VTOL aircraft when only a few feet above the ground were double the jet thrust, it might accelerate at this height over soft, uneven terrain until aerodynamic lift made up the balance.

Civil application of VTOL must be preceded by substantial noise reduction, which for lift engines whose thrust exceeds the aircraft weight appears very difficult unless the thrust is achieved by accelerating rather large amounts of air to only moderate speeds as in the rotorcraft. However, limitation in rotorcraft speeds is one of the factors that make it difficult to match fixed-wing economics at present and it is possible that quiet, economic operation between city centres will become possible only when the undoubtedly extreme difficulty of retracting the rotor into the fuselage of a conventional aircraft shape has been overcome.

Automatic control

Finally, it is worth observing that the increases in reliability of automatic control equipment, and reductions in its weight, foreseeable from a combination of microminiaturization and redundancy in circuit design, may make possible a new sort of flying, in which all routine control and decision-making is done by a computer, and only the exceptional situation that seems to require the exercise of human judgement is referred to the pilot. If experience with such 'super-reliable' circuitry ultimately leads airworthiness authorities to accept aerodynamically unstable aircraft – designs that would be unstable if the control system were to fail – economies should be possible, since present designs are substantially comprised by stability considerations.

Reader participation

The problem of deciding how the range of different technological possibilities and of conceivable future patterns of market needs that have been described in this article will combine to determine the aviation scene in 1984 is left as an exercise to the reader.

TRAVELLING BY AIR IN 1984

by Pierre Satre

Technical Manager, Sud-Aviation

The development of commercial air transport depends upon two factors. First, general economic progress and international relations result in increasing demand, and the continuing response of the air transport companies must lead to improved service to passengers at lower rates. Secondly, technical advances enable operators to benefit from better performance of the aircraft used – the term 'performance' embracing the entire range of operational characteristics, including the operating cost. These factors are interconnected. The increasing demand stimulates the creation of improved machines. The use of new aircraft, of higher performance, means that more and more clients will make use of air transport.

Figure 1 shows the progress made in world air transport between 1945 and 1962, according to ICAO statistics. Can we, from such a graph, calculate the probable increase in air transport during the next twenty years ? We do not propose to do so here, as we shall consider only the technical aspect of the problem. One thing is, however, certain: the demand will continue to grow. To promote this growth, it will not suffice simply to increase the speed. Mass transportation, at lower fares, will also be a goal, and the air traveller will be offered much more frequent services and more convenient schedules.

Technical progress

The factors governing progress are to be found both in the improvement in the existing concepts and in the introduction of new ones. If, by their very nature, the latter defy forecast, one can nevertheless note the very great acceleration in the rate of technical progress made during the past few decades. It took forty years, from the time of the first closed circuit flight, for aircraft to reach the speed of sound in level flight; then a further five years to double this speed. Five years after that, we reached orbital speed. If, however, we consider only transport *on our planet*, there are two factors which will lessen and ultimately limit the increase in supersonic speeds:

(1) The cost of the more advanced aircraft is such that airlines demand a service life of at least ten years or even fifteen, to allow for reasonable amortization. Thus, the first supersonic aircraft, the Concorde, of SUD-BAC, scheduled to enter service at the beginning of the next decade, will be operating at least until the year 1980, and the last aircraft in the series will be operating for a considerably longer period than that.

(2) The size of our planet is such that there is no point in increasing the speed beyond a certain limit (especially when it is considered that the time the traveller has to spend on the ground is by no means diminishing at the same rate as that of the flying time).

Evolution of DOC

The Direct Operating Cost is the airline's outlay for the flight as such – that is, apart from all the additional expenses of a commercial nature. Expressed in terms of currency per seat offered and per mile flown, it varies according to the stage length. The DOC is a good criterion of technical progress.

If we now include, in one and the same graph (Figure 2), the curves relating to typical transport aircraft at different periods, we are struck by the continuous trend towards lower rates. This reduction can be explained by the fact that the DOC varies inversely with the speed and the capacity of the aircraft – factors which have always been increasing since air transport began. This increase will continue over the next twenty years.

Other service improvements

Under pressure of the demand, the airlines will be compelled to make numerous improvements in their services, improvements by which the traveller will benefit directly and, again, indirectly by the effect of these improvements on the operating cost. Thus, *reduction in the turn-around times* (by a further study of the non-technical 'handling' services such as the cleaning of the aircraft)

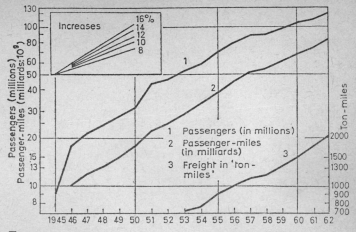

FIG. 1

Progress of world air transport from 1945 to 1962 according to ICAO statistics. This graph has been prepared with a log scale for the ordinates so that the direction of the curves indicates the increase in traffic as a percentage. Thus between 1958 and 1962 the average annual increase in ton-miles was 8·5 per cent for passengers, 11 per cent for passenger-miles, and 16 per cent for freight.

will allow an increase in aircraft utilization, and therefore in the number of hours flown per annum. Similarly we can expect *reduction in the holding times* before landing, which are very costly for the operator and most unpleasant for the passenger. I will add, in this connexion, that in my opinion the essential advantage of the vertical take-off aircraft, if it becomes a commercial proposition, does not lie, as is commonly believed, in the possibility of arriving and departing near the city centres. That is an illusory advantage. Instead, VTOL will allow, perhaps, a large number of simultaneous take-offs and landings at one and the same airport, and this would represent real progress.

The application of ' *economy* ' fares to local services, at off-peak periods, and the extension of air-shuttle services at specified times without reservations, are two steps which, while they will probably bring in many new passengers, will again increase the load factors and the utilization rates of the aircraft.

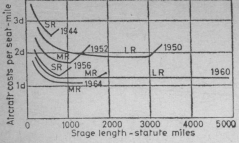

FIG. 2

Direct operating cost versus stage length for typical transport aeroplanes from 1944 to 1964. SR: short range; MR: medium range;
LR: long range.

For some years past, the increasing importance of *regularity* of
service has been recognized by both aircraft manufacturers and
airlines. Regularity depends mainly upon technical advance, and
we can be sure that considerable progress in this field will be made
during the next twenty years. On the one hand, the study of
reliability, a new science which has developed as a result of space
research, will allow reduction in the number of failures and of
slight incidents which delay flights or immobilize the aircraft,
while they will at the same time lead to the lowering of maintenance costs. On the other hand, the improvements in navigation
methods – the Doppler system, and afterwards the inertial system,
improvements in very short-term weather forecasting (through
the use of satellites) and especially *all-weather landing systems* such
as Sud-Lear Siegler – will reduce the number of cancelled flights
or diversions and will ensure almost 100 per cent regularity of
flight, irrespective of season or latitude.

I will also mention here the expected increase in the use of computers and automatic checking systems, which will relieve present
burdens on the pilots.

Specialized aircraft

The design of specialized aircraft according to the route pattern
and the volume of traffic is one of the ways in which one is tempted
to go to obtain lower fares. The advantage gained, however, by
this specialization must be sufficiently important to meet the

competition of: (1) down-graded aircraft which, while not so well adapted, has the advantage of a purchase price which is often very low; or (2) new multi-purpose aircraft whereby the operator does not get quite 100 per cent benefit in each mission but which is, in the end, more profitable, thanks to the saving made by standardization of aircraft and spare parts.

Transport aircraft in 1984

Bearing in mind the foregoing, *and considering only the concepts in course of development during 1963*, let me try to outline the characteristic features of the airline fleets in 1984.

(1) *Almost exclusive use of jets on all routes*. Although, at present, in the minority (18 per cent of the number of aircraft, but more than 50 per cent of the productive capacity), jets will gradually preponderate in all fleets. The turbo-prop aircraft will see their share reduced as a result of constant progress in fuel consumption made by turbofan engines.

(2) *A large majority of supersonic aircraft on long-range services*. Cruising at speeds from Mach 2.2 (1,260 knots) to Mach 3.5 (2,000 knots), supersonic aircraft will be used on long transcontinental and transoceanic routes. The Antipodes will be reached in six to seven hours' flying time. The types of aircraft in service will be the Concorde and the future American supersonic aircraft.

Supersonic aircraft on medium-range services

The operational flexibility of supersonic aircraft of the Concorde type will be such that the airlines operating them on long-range routes will also fly them on the medium-range extensions of their networks. In the U.S.A., direct coast-to-coast links will be provided by aircraft of this type.

A wide range of types on all other routes

According to the size of the airlines and the areas served, the volume of traffic and the length of each stage, we shall see in use short-take-off aircraft, subsonic and supersonic aircraft, aircraft of a seating capacity of 40 to 200 passengers, two-, three-, and four-jet aircraft. Turbo-prop aircraft may perhaps continue to be used either for cargo transport on long hauls where they will be justified by a saving in fuel, or on very short ranges, for the short-take-off aircraft, because the use of propellers is an important factor where slow-speed flight and short landing distance are concerned.

Positive increase in freight transport

The tendency, indicated in the graph in Figure 1, will become more marked and freight transport will be a growing item in airline revenues. This development will be spurred by the designing of new aircraft, turbo-prop and jet, which, thanks to their technical refinements, will make it possible to reduce prices still further.

Conclusions

Whatever anyone may say, the quest for higher speeds constitutes a major incentive to progress in air transport. The study of the technical problems raised by supersonic aircraft contributes, indirectly and with a time lag but nevertheless undeniably, to progress in all aircraft, by increased knowledge of all aspects of manufacture and flying. To take a recent example, the gas-turbine was developed, in the first instance, to achieve higher speeds, yet it is used today in all new models of transport aircraft, including the slowest, and it is thanks to the gas-turbine that the helicopter has become a most useful machine.

Progress in materials, in constructional methods, in propulsion, in reliability, in methods of control and navigation, in landing systems – in fact all this progress, *stimulated by supersonic aircraft* – will be found, in one form or another, in all the aircraft constituting the fleets of 1984, throughout the whole range of speeds. It is, in part, thanks to it, that qualities of safety, regularity, flexibility in operation, and economy of this equipment will achieve a very high level, which, in turn, will ensure the continuous development of air transport.

TOWARDS COMPLETE SAFETY IN THE AIR

by R. M. Macdonnell

Secretary-General, International Civil Aviation Organization, Montreal

Any glance over the technical aspects of air transportation in 1984 must pause at the problem of safety. Safety, of course, is relative;

today's accident rates would have been regarded as unexpectedly
low by the airline pioneers of thirty years ago, and even ten years
ago the fatality rate was nearly twice as high as it was in 1962. Yet
the total number of airline passengers killed in 1952 was only
386, while in the so-called 'best' safety year of 1962 the number
was 765.

The reason, of course, is the yearly increase in the number of
people who fly. ICAO's statisticians anticipate that 1984's air
traffic will be three or four times as great as today's. If this should
prove to be the case, and unless there is a radical decrease in the
accident rate, the mounting total of passenger fatalities may produce a public reaction which could seriously injure air transportation. From this it would seem that the first aviation requirement
for the developing technology of the next two decades is the
improvement of air safety. Let us consider some of the ways in
which this improvement is likely to come about.

The first requirement is the removal of that greatest cause of
accidents: human error. Human error can mean a pilot's mis-
judgement in landing, a traffic controller's miscalculation, a
mechanic's failure to insert a lock washer in a critical assembly. In
twenty years it may well be possible to avoid human error completely. Much of the answer will be in automation. Even today it is
possible to land an aircraft without human hands at the controls;
it is probable that the pilot of 1984 will still make the decisions, but
that his aircraft will do the mechanical things for itself – will fly
itself, navigate itself, take off and land by itself. The problem now
is in reliability, in our present inability to build electronic equipment which can operate for a sufficient length of time without the
possibility of failure. We get around this problem to some extent
today by what we call redundancy, by using two or three pieces of
similar equipment – when one piece fails, the next one takes over,
and so on – but this technique is expensive and the extra weight to
be carried often rules it out as a possibility. New developments in
solid-state physics, the use of the transistor, the ability to incorporate a multitude of electronic circuits in a minute sliver of
material, the elimination of the heat put out by thermionic valves
– all of these promise the ability to build inexpensive, light-weight
electronic equipment with many back-up circuits, so that if one or
even more than one should fail there are always other circuits to

take up the responsibility. In fact, it is even possible to anticipate the construction of electronic equipment which requires no servicing for the life of the aircraft.

In aviation history, small maintenance errors have frequently produced appalling results. This problem too, must yield to automation. A precedent is already available in the automatic inspection devices used in the United States before missile launchings. I can conceive of a similar device built into each aircraft, allowing a speedy, exhaustive, and accurate inspection of every critical point and, among other things, catching any defects due to maintenance or wear. I would also expect that by then we would have a better theoretical knowledge of metal fatigue and an ability to design most fatigue defects out of our engines and airframes. In the few places where these defects will still exist, mechanical redundancy may also be called upon.

Other aspects and results of automation will show in air traffic control and communications. Today, an air traffic controller's job is a combination of tedium and action; he has many moments of routine, keeping track of aircraft movements, for each moment when he must make an intelligent decision. It will be the role of the computer to take away the routine functions of the controller, to keep a record of each aircraft's movements and the possibility of infringement upon another aircraft's airspace; it will free the controller for his important work, which is the use of his experience and judgement to keep traffic flowing smoothly and efficiently, and to avoid collision. A reliable airborne collision avoidance device would, of course, simplify traffic control procedure greatly, but there seems to be valid doubt that such a device will be available even in twenty years.

We can expect a mixed bag of transport aircraft by 1984, including long-range supersonics, medium-range supersonic jets, and short- and long-range VTOLs (vertical take off and landing), and our air traffic control system will have to be able to handle the different varieties. Accurate navigational equipment will be supplied, either self-contained inertial-type or a ground-based, worldwide, low-frequency radio chain. The traffic control computer will know the whereabouts of the aircraft at all times. As long as the aircraft stays with its flight plan, the computer will keep its changing position in mind; as soon as there is a significant deviation from the flight plan, the aeroplane will automatically report this deviation to the computer to keep its knowledge up-to-date.

All this presupposes an improvement in our present air-to-ground communications facilities, now somewhat overloaded. The possible abandonment of routine position-reporting will help to ease this strain, but in addition we shall have to go to much higher radio frequencies, and rely upon communications satellites to relay the line-of-sight messages beyond the horizon to the traffic control centre.

The simplification in air-to-ground communication will result in far more need for communication between points on the ground. The computers in adjacent traffic control centres will have to keep in touch at all times. This means that we shall not be able to rely on communications channels which can be affected by the vagaries of the ionosphere – and this rules out the HF band. The alternatives are either land-line relays or satellite relays, in both cases using microwaves with multi-channel capabilities. Another possibility, and one which shows perhaps the most interesting promise, is the laser; one laser band, operating through silvered plastic tubes running under the ocean from Europe to America, could carry all the communications now being carried on radio frequencies, and still have room for several thousands of television channels.

Along with human error and insufficient traffic control capabilities, unexpected weather is an important item in today's accident reports. We can certainly look forward to a vastly improved weather reporting and forecasting system. We are now, with the appearance of meteorological satellites, on the threshold of a great advance in the field; for the first time we shall have accurate reports on weather conditions in many parts of the globe where there are no reporting networks and, from these 'actual weather' reports, I think we can reasonably expect a considerable improvement in our knowledge of why the weather behaves as it does. Even today computers can predict expected weather as well as human forecasters; with better theoretical knowledge, we may expect by 1984 that forecasting will be in the hands of the machines, leaving only meteorological research for humans.

Weather 'actuals' rather than forecasts will then be the key to aeronautical meteorology. With weather satellites to give us a true, constantly changing picture and with computers integrating this information constantly instead of – as at present – at six-hour intervals, with other new reporting devices, and with automatic interrogation of aircraft in flight whenever the computers need the information, we can expect good, moment-to-moment knowledge of both upper-air and surface conditions. Oddly enough, as forecasting improves it will become less important, for flight times will become shorter, with three hours coming close to maximum. (True, the London–Australia run by non-stop supersonic aircraft would come close to twice this time, but I suspect that even by 1984 the fuel load needed for such an operation will make the non-stop flight uneconomical.) In other words our knowledge of actual weather conditions will be so accurate, our needs for forecasts will cover so short a period, that in effect we shall be able to remove the element of surprise from meteorology.

This leaves only one major meteorological problem: clear-air turbulence. So far the causes are unknown, but the effects on high-speed aircraft can be disastrous. All that can be said at the moment is that we hope to be able to predict the presence of clear-air turbulence before 1984: certainly if we do not succeed, high-speed flight will not be as safe as it should be.

This has been a short review of some of the basic improvements we can expect in the field of air safety twenty years hence. These improvements will be costly. We shall need so much more than we have at present in the way of air navigation aids and facilities – and yet, even today, our basic problems in many parts of the world arise from an insufficiency of trained men coupled with an insufficiency of funds. Much is now being done to improve the supply of technicians; many less-developed countries are running their own training plans in addition to those operated by ICAO for the United Nations Special Fund and as projects under the United Nations Technical Assistance programme. Yet the demands of aviation continue to grow from year to year, and we come no closer to fulfilling them: like Lewis Carroll's Red Queen we have to run as hard as we can to stay where we are. Unless this situation improves radically in the next twenty years, 1984 will have the technical knowledge to produce complete air safety, yet accidents will still occur.

Surface Transport

THE PROSPECTS FOR HOVER TRANSPORT

by C. S. Cockerell
Hovercraft Development Ltd

If an engineer looks out of the window and lets his mind take in the scene of trees and bushes and grass, he may note that these things evolved by nature over millions of years are not stiff, but are designed to sway in the breeze. And yet man's idea of a ship is something stiff and strong, and capable of resisting the forces which are largely the result of its stiffness. Does this mean that we shall move out of this present era of 'granite' engineering and towards engineering forms which yield to the forces to which they are subjected?

If one goes out of the room and up the stairs, one cannot help comparing the quality of the balancing and control mechanisms of a man with the primitive performances of a bumpy bus, a swaying train, or a pitching ship. Does this mean that one of the aspects of engineering which will receive more attention in the next twenty years is control systems?

Again, consider the number of bits in a mile of railway line, or the number of doors, wheels, springs, bearings, and other things in a passenger train. As we move towards a press-button age, certainly one of the things which will receive more and more attention is designing for the lowest possible maintenance costs.

It is just such ideas and such advances which have got to be developed by the hovercraft engineer, and put over to engineers who are familiar with 'stiff' engineering, and stability as it comes. A hovercraft is an attempt to extend the uses of a surface vehicle for operation over soft surfaces such as mud and water, and over unprepared tracks, including the sea. To do this, it has to borrow ideas from almost all other forms of vehicle, extend them, and add a few of its own.

What does it offer? As a start: the carriage of large numbers of

passengers and cars, and some freight, over stretches of water like
the Solent or the English Channel, at speeds of twice to five times
that of a ship ferry, and at about the same fares. The first commercial service is likely to be from the mainland of England to the Isle
of Wight, and indeed it has recently been announced that a new
operating company is being formed for this purpose, the plan
being to open a service in the spring of 1967. This innovation
should help to ease the present summer congestion brought about
by the rapid rate of traffic growth on these routes. A hovercraft
for the Solent service would carry about two dozen cars, and be of
about 100 tons gross weight, and it has to operate over Solent seas,
which are normally 2 ft or less, and only occasionally as much as
5 ft. For such a craft the conditions would be easy, using existing
techniques in the building of a flexible suspension system below the
body of the craft composed of flexible materials and air-curtains.
The success of this venture therefore depends primarily upon the
soundness of the engineering of all the various pieces of rotating
machinery.

The next stage will be a hoverferry across the English Channel
in the Dover–Calais area, and here sea and wind conditions are
much more difficult. It is on these Channel routes that we are
likely to see the gradual evolution of the hovercraft, much as has
happened with both ship ferries and cross-Channel aircraft.

By 1970 a modified Solent hoverferry should be in operation
across the Channel. This is likely to be augmented two or three
years later by larger craft designed to carry about 100 cars, and
fitted with anti-roll and anti-pitch control systems, which will
give a much improved ride. A great deal of development remains
to be done in evolving more efficient controlled suspension systems having lower drags over rough water; in propulsion systems;
and in structures. And all these features are likely to be greatly
improved in 1984, resulting in improvements in efficiency and
lower running costs – sufficiently low, in fact, to make hovercraft
an embarrassment to a Channel Tunnel, should it be built, rather
than the Tunnel being an embarrassment to the hovercraft.

A 70-knot, 100-car hovercraft would be capable of doing the
same amount of work as about four or five conventional Dover–
Calais ship-ferries, so that as a unit it is too large for certain other
routes; but it will be possible from the experience gained in the

design of such craft to undertake the more difficult design of smaller craft with the same seakeeping ability and suitable for routes with lower traffic flows.

If the standard of living of the developed countries is doubled by 1984, it seems likely that the number of people able and wishing to travel across the ocean may increase by perhaps ten times, and there may therefore be a case for an open-water hoverliner – the

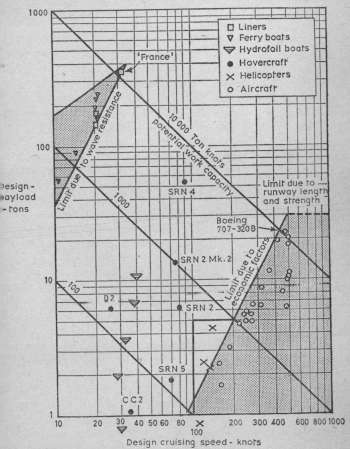

FIG. I
Operating characteristics of various types of craft.

argument being that a ship would be too slow and an air fare too expensive. Certainly if there is a real need for mass transport, open-water hovercraft will appear, but probably not by 1984. It is interesting to note that, whereas the case for a nuclear ship must be based on economics, a large hovercraft, while capable of carrying the weight of a fully-shielded reactor, would be able to offer both increased speed and increased range.

The other main application of hovercraft to a developed country is the tracked hovercar of 50 to 250 tons, as a high-speed city-centre to city-centre transport. At some speed around 100 knots wheels begin to reach their limit, and are more efficiently replaced by the sliding motion of an air cushion running on a concrete track. Having changed over to an air cushion, the practical limit in speed depends on the one hand upon the deflections and the maintained alignment of the track; and on the other hand, the amount of 'black magic' built into the suspension system of the air-cushion pad. Civil engineering studies on the track and suspension and control system studies on the hovercar indicate that the practical limit of speed, taking into account the economics, is perhaps 300 knots, and may be higher, and that the power involved per passenger is only about a fifth of that of an aircraft of the same speed.

It would seem that an elevated track is essential on the score of safety, and to prevent small boys throwing old bicycles on the track just to see what happens. The conventional solution to maintaining track alignment would be screw jacks and shims, but 1984 engineering and the drive for lower maintenance costs call for a system where the track is coated with an inch or two of some suitable material, and 'machined' true by a special maintenance craft travelling at speed from time to time. Since the hovercar will not touch the track and therefore will not wear the track, this conception really does belong to 1984, in contrast with some of the 1884 conceptions of existing railway engineering.

Our present knowledge of civil engineering, control systems engineering, autosignalling, aerodynamics, linear motors, and air cushion engineering would enable such a new form of overland transport to be brought into being before 1984. But there are problems of finance, wayleaves, legal matters, nationalized monopolies, etc. If progress depended solely upon the technical factors involved, there could be a hovercar system in existence by 1984.

THE RAILWAYS OF TOMORROW

by Camille Martin
Société Nationale des Chemins de Fer Français, Paris

The railways, which came into being in the middle of the nine-teenth century, played a large part in the industrial revolution, and they have made a great contribution to human progress. At the end of the Second World War there were some who thought that the railways might gradually lose their pre-eminence to youthful competitors, the roads and the airways; in the opinion of the public at large and of many statesmen, the supremacy of the railways was a thing of the past. Very soon, however – and sooner in the developing countries than in the industrially advanced countries – this view had to be modified as a result of a better understanding of the transport requirements to be satisfied, the suitability and limitations of all the methods available, their real running and investment costs, and their opportunities for exploiting new technical developments.

The railway is particularly suited for the heavy hauls of today and tomorrow: whether it is a question of peak holiday transport during the summer or winter or the daily flow of commuters, the unit to be considered is of the order of 100,000 passengers; about 100 trains are sufficient to handle it. Similarly, 100 or so goods trains are sufficient to supply the daily needs of a large industrial complex. Although certain routes are at present used intensively, and, to meet recent expansion in the amount of traffic, demand new construction, there is as yet no sign of a limit being reached in technical developments which might curtail the advantages offered by railways or the possibility of maintaining, over the profitable routes, a very low cost per ton-kilometre.

It is, of course, true that all methods of transport are able to take advantage of technical progress in respect of increases in power, speed, profitability, and economy. But the characteristics of rail-ways enable them to do so to particular advantage.

The separation of the locomotive from the rolling stock curtails the trouble of laying out the power unit and enables many forms of energy to be used. Steam engines fired by coal or fuel oil, diesel engines, gas turbines, d.c. or a.c. electric motors – all of these may be used for haulage and, if nuclear power or fuel cells come into general industrial use, we may be certain that the railways will be among the first to reap their benefits.

The guidance of wheels by rails presents traffic problems in a linear, one-dimensional sense, which, for the road vehicle or ship, involve two dimensions, or three for the aircraft or rocket. This results in a relative ease of traffic control on railways and is certainly not unrelated to the high factor of safety and regularity of rail transport.

Finally, railways constitute a self-contained system, not only on a national scale but on a continental level. As such, it is well suited to the application of those techniques of control and optimization that are sometimes called cybernetics.

Such are the facts and the prospects of the railways today, in the light of which we may allow ourselves, without too much risk, to prophesy their future during the next twenty years.

Japan has already found the answer to her traffic requirements in the construction of the celebrated Tokaido line which specializes in express traffic at speeds in excess of 200 km/hr, leaving the old lines to slower traffic. Railways elsewhere will undoubtedly adopt similar solutions by 1984. The new railways of Europe will be more direct and more unified than today, thanks to such links as the Channel Tunnel, the Messina Bridge, and the new low-altitude tunnels through the Alps, and to the solution of the problems presented by variations in gauges between some countries.

The new high-speed lines will not look very unusual, with their broken-stone ballast and sleepers of plasticized wood or concrete which carry vibration-damped continuous steel rails; the arts of metallurgy and soil-mechanics which ensure permanence to the qualities of this track between maintenance inspections limited to intervals of five years are not visible to the eyes of the layman. All signals have disappeared, and are replaced by cables laid parallel to the track which fulfil the functions of waveguides for numerous ultra-short-wave telecommunication channels and enable the position, speed, and forward movement of trains to be controlled and telephone communication to be made between passengers and stations or other trains, as well as between the central operations controller and the engine-driver. The latter will be more of a chief engineer, responsible for watching his instrument panel (temperature gauges, vibration analysers, stress recorders, etc.) and for taking carefully defined remedial action in the case of deviations or faults.

The equipment for programmed operation and control will differ very little as between locomotives powered by gas turbines and electric locomotives. The latter will be much the commonest in Europe, as the shortfall in power which threatens the most populated areas will result in priority being given to investments which make the best use of available energy sources. What will be the source of the current carried by the overhead cables, closely resembling those of 1964 ? The train driver is as little concerned about the source of his fuel as is the motorist; it is very probable that the production of electric power will be shared almost equally between coal, nuclear power, fuel oil, natural gas, and water-power supplied by rivers and the tides.

Internal combustion engines of medium power will continue to be used on secondary routes where it is desired to maintain a good return on services which are not used to full capacity. Experiments in the use of fuel cells for independent electric traction are still being carried on but, just as the ultra-light battery has remained only a dream for a century, so this other electro-chemical technique will still have only limited application for transport purposes, by reason of its very low power-to-weight ratio.

Passenger rolling-stock will be well streamlined and give an air of extreme comfort: carriage springing will ensure good adhesion to the track during rapid acceleration, coaches will be well sound-proofed, and travellers will be able to shop on the train. For some, the journey will be a very pleasant relaxation, and for others it will offer a comfortable atmosphere in which to work.

Goods traffic will have undergone fundamental changes by the introduction of automatic couplings, not so much because of the size of trains as of the possibilities offered by electronic data-processing of orders and information relating to the distribution and identification of trucks and to the composition, movement, and uncoupling of train-sets. The making out of a way-bill will be sufficient to ensure the magnetic docketing of the truck concerned and to commence the chain of coded information which will set in motion all operations necessary for its routing without the need of any human intervention – other than the authorization for its departure from the marshalling yard or station sidings and the phone call which is traditionally made out of courtesy to the consignee to inform him that his truck will be available to him in two hours' time, information which will, in the normal course of events, already have been transmitted to his teleprinter.

As for operations at the point of arrival, these will have put an end to the shocking wastage involved in the transfer of goods entailed by periods of useless shunting for twenty-four or forty-eight hours during each transfer. All heavy merchandise in bulk, from minerals to granulated sugar, will travel in special hopper cases which can be unloaded in a matter of seconds. All finished products of small unit bulk will be concentrated in containers or in semi-articulated trailers, the unloading of which will hardly take longer. Even for agricultural produce, semi-manufactured stack-loaded articles, or complex equipment loaded in roofed trucks or wagons with sliding doors, it is to be hoped that the costs and delays will be very much reduced.

So much for the customer, but what about the railway employees ? They will be less numerous than in the past – and yet there will be more than a million in Europe. The conscientiousness with which they had already provided an indispensable public service will be reinforced by a much more complete participation by even the lowest grades in work carried out under much better conditions, and by the disappearance of laborious, dirty, and dangerous jobs.

The stoker's shovel, the labourer's riveting-hammer, the straightening bar of the workers on the permanent way, and the uncoupling tackle of the shunting yardsman will no longer be employed in 1984. Does this mean that the railways, as we know them, will cease to be recognizable ? Of the four principles instituted by the pioneers, namely, steam power, the employment of steel to steel adhesion, movement in trains, and guidance by contact, the last three named will still constitute the stamp of the railways' originality and the source of their progress.

ROADS AND TRAFFIC IN 1984

by Sir William Glanville, F.R.S.

Director of Road Research Department of Scientific and Industrial Research

Existing roads and those we are building today seem certain to form a large part of the road network on which we will be driving in twenty years' time, although it is to be expected that the vehicles of today, unlike those veterans of pre-1920, will have been consigned to the scrapheap. The demand for transport of all kinds will grow, and there will be a fuller coordination of all systems.

Sources of power may change and manufacturing costs lessen, but we must look to a future dominated by the road vehicle. It has been estimated that by 1984 the number of vehicles licensed in Britain will rise from the present level of 12 million to 25 million, of which 18 million will be cars. In some parts of the country, roads are already overloaded and, although new major roads and motorways will take a large amount of the traffic forecast, it is clear that the problem of congestion will remain. On the one hand there will be increasing pressure to find ways of ensuring the best possible use of existing roads, and on the other to plan the most economical ways of meeting demand. Longer peak-hour travel periods may be coupled to shorter hours of work.

Goods vehicles may be larger and cars may be smaller. It is inconceivable also that public transport vehicles – buses and coaches – and their mode of operation will remain as at present. Special facilities on high-speed roads and at terminal points can be expected to come into use. With the nuisances of fumes and noise considerably abated, if not eliminated, and with improved road-user discipline, the atmosphere and environment in our cities will have greatly improved.

There are no major physical difficulties in the construction of inter-urban roads. By the early 1970s, Britain's comprehensive rural motorway network of about 1,000 miles linking the main centres of population and trade should be substantially complete, and by 1984 this mileage will have been extended considerably.

Everywhere it is recognized that the major problem will continue to be that of urban traffic. In twenty years' time some large urban-road schemes can be expected to be completed and others will be in hand, on a far greater scale than is now contemplated. The reports published early in 1964 of the Buchanan Working Group and the Crowther Steering Group on Traffic in Towns have painted a broad canvas, showing that there is no one easy and complete solution to the problem caused by the explosive growth of motor traffic. It is, however, clear from the reception given to the Buchanan report that society is at least beginning to realize that new concepts of urban living and transport are necessary. By 1984 it is to be expected that we will have Buchanan-type ideals of block redevelopment proceeding on an increasing scale, although it is not to be expected that the problem of how to satisfy the demands of the vehicle and to maintain good standards of environment will be solved from an economic point of view.

Urban motorways will stretch towards, if not into, the hearts of our cities, and segregation of the people from the vehicle will have occurred on a much larger scale. Although it seems hardly likely that large areas of our cities will be banned for the use of traffic completely, restrictions and some form of sharing in the use of vehicles will inevitably be forced, increasingly, upon the community. Parking and garaging vehicles, and dealing with the 'ends of journeys' generally, will continue to present a problem in built-up areas.

The rapid technical progress of the electronics industry in the last twenty years and its potential for the future leave little doubt that it will have a great impact on road transport. The control of vehicles and traffic are obvious fields of application. Electronic systems have been shown to be capable of the completely automatic steering and control of vehicles but they have yet to be developed to a sufficient degree of reliability to justify replacement of human guidance. However, 1984 could see long stretches of additional lanes on some of our motorways having built-in guidance and detector cables to be used in conjunction with vehicles equipped with sensing devices. This system would enable drivers to receive and act upon warning messages from other vehicles about changes in speed, direction, and position of preceding and following vehicles far earlier than our present limitation of direct and reflected views of hand or mechanical signals, or unannounced changes of speed or direction.

Progress with simpler systems for automatic control will come first. For example, visual or audio warning devices to guide drivers in fog or to warn them of obstruction or potential dangers ahead will be fairly commonplace. Another aspect of automatic control which is now the subject of research will, without doubt, be in operation within twenty years; this involves the control by a single computer of the road traffic in the busier parts of our cities. By automatic control of large numbers of detectors and traffic signals, the computer will be continuously assessing the traffic position over an area and organizing it to obtain the most efficient flow.

A leading American authority has, in fact, predicted in a recent lecture that, by 1980, electronic and other driver aids will increase highway capacity by a half, increase average speed by a half and cut accident rates by a half. Whether this is achieved or not there will certainly be great advances in dealing with the problems of vehicle stability and control. Improved riding quality, better braking, using anti-locking devices, and improved tyres are already coming into use, and we may expect to see further improvements which will greatly reduce skidding and loss of control, perhaps to negligible proportions.

Inside the cars of 1984, the greatest changes are likely to be in the controls and in increased passenger protection. For controlling the vehicle, gear changing (if, indeed, it is still necessary) will be automatic, and if the lead of the aircraft industry is followed there will be no need for any direct link between the driver and the control surfaces. The steering wheel may well disappear and be replaced by a system which gives the driver a truer sense of the forces acting on his vehicle, and which will help to make it more certain that his actions in an emergency will be the correct ones.

The next twenty years will doubtless see the further development of new forms of land transport such as the hovercraft, and monorail vehicles, and travelling belts, but there seems little prospect that these will completely or even largely replace the motor vehicle, with its great advantages to the individual.

HOW BIG WILL SHIPS BECOME?

by Professor Yoshihiro Watanabe

Faculty of Engineering, Kyushu University, Japan

It is sometimes said that the future of ships is not promising, yet there is a good prospect of further improvement in both the quantity and quality of them, because the present total tonnage of ships in the world has grown to about twice what it was before the war, while intercontinental trade and transportation are increasing year by year. Japanese estimates of the gross tonnage of ships of the world by 1970 give a figure of 170 million tons.

The lines of improvement in modern ships are: (1) larger ships, (2) higher speeds, (3) more economic operation, (4) better navigation, (5) greater comfort and safety, and (6) greater reliability. By these trends, ships are changing for the better. If we look back over past changes, we see that it is not impossible to foresee the actual outward appearance of future ships.

Shipbuilding is based on the synthesis of many branches of technology, and history tells us that advances in shipbuilding technique have occurred as a result of progress in materials, power, and means of propulsion – and also with social conditions. Sometimes the changes have been revolutionary, as a result of entirely new ideas in these related fields.

Generally speaking, one recent tendency has been for ships to become specialized types, such as ore-carriers and tankers, and this tendency will be intensified further until the differences between the types are very marked. For example, ore-carriers, tankers, and similar kinds of ships will increase in size, as far as operating economy allows, with increase in speed being of rather secondary importance. With passenger ships, comfort and safety are primary considerations but speed is not far behind.

Size and materials

Technically, the available materials limit the size of a ship. Essential requirements for shipbuilding materials are that they should be very strong, tough, produced in large quantity, and cheap in price. Steel is the only material meeting all these requirements at present. The strength-to-weight ratio of a material is generally one of the factors used to judge it, and even in a steel ship there is an upper limit in size if only ordinary mild steel is used. Since before the war, the size of a tanker has grown from 15,000 to 100,000 tons. The largest ship at present is 132,000 deadweight tons (displacement, 163,367 tons), *Nissho-maru*, in which maximum thickness of mild steel plate is 40 mm.

Use of lighter construction is now permitted by the recent relaxation of classification rules, but the maximum size for a ship of mild steel will never go beyond 150,000 deadweight tons.

Special steel would be necessary for one larger than that. At present, steel of 60 kg per sq. mm. tensile strength is available and sometimes used, though not widely because of its high price. 70 and 80 kg steels are also being developed. However, buckling and deflection of structures are controlled by the stiffness of a material, and the stiffness of these special steels remains the same as mild steel. It will, therefore, become necessary in the future to create a specially stiff shipbuilding material or to find new methods of construction.

Aluminium will be more widely used for the sake of its high strength-to-weight ratio in superstructure and the like, but not in main hull of a large ship because of its high price and limited production.

Apart from these technical considerations, it is generally believed that a larger ship pays better. It is, however, known that the merit of a larger ship at present attains a maximum at, say, about 90,000 deadweight tons, showing a decrease above that. There are also obstacles to be considered in the forms of harbour accommodation, water depth, and others. According to a research made by the Mitsubishi Company, the most suitable size and shaft horsepower of a contemporary tanker, corresponding to given draught, are as shown in Figure 1.

All these considerations will be greatly subjected to the changes in social and economic circumstances, but, on the whole, it may be proper to put the maximum size of the bulk carrier in future as approximately 200,000 deadweight tons.

Power and speed

It is said that this is the age of an energy revolution. The major source of energy for present-day ships is oil. Nuclear power is

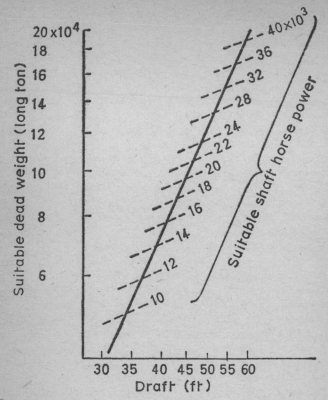

Fig. 1

coming to the fore, but the thermal efficiency of the fission-energy steam-turbine system, which is the scheme now under consideration, is rather low, and unless a more efficient and safer method can be developed we may doubt if nuclear energy can be made useful and profitable in the near future for commercial shipping, even for passenger ships.

Oil is now widely used in boiler-turbine and diesel engines. With the use of steam of higher pressure and higher temperature in the former, and with higher mean indicated pressure and higher grade supercharging in the latter, the volume and weight of engine for a given horsepower are being reduced greatly – in the case of diesels being now about one half of what they were before the war. Consequently, the earning capacity of a ship has considerably increased and this, combined with reduced hull weight and improvements in hull form (such as the bulbous bow), has resulted in increases in payload or speed. Changes in the ratio of dead-weight (cargo capacity) to displacement (weight of the ship) are shown in Figure 2, while the economical speeds of tankers in present conditions are as shown in Figure 3 – from which it can be deduced that the speed of large bulk carriers of the future will not be remarkably high, perhaps 20 knots at the most.

The highest speed of general cargo ships at present is about 20 knots, which may rise to 30 knots in the future. But it is probable that most of them will be gradually replaced by freighter aircraft. Passenger ships will serve only as vessels for pleasure cruises and will run at about 40 knots at most. For short-distance ferries, we can expect quite different orders of speed, for which hydrofoils, hovercraft, and the like will be greatly developed to make 80 or 90 knots.

Handling

For comfort and safety, easy manoeuvring, especially with large ships, and minimum rolling and pitching are necessary. To meet such requirements, many devices are proposed, for example bow thrusters, water 'brakes' to arrest forward motion, stabilizing fins and tanks, and so on. Even though they are not fully used now because of their extra weight and cost, in the future there will be more urgent demand for these devices and others, and they will be fitted in cargo ships as well as passenger ships. Cargo handling equipment will be taken off the ships and deployed only on land.

Automatic control arrangements

In the total operating cost of a ship, about 15 per cent goes to man it, and this points to the necessity of reducing the number of crew. For this purpose, various types of remote automatic control are being introduced in ships as in other industries. For example, a cargo ship lately built in Japan has electronic computers for the main and auxiliary engines installed in one control room, where the engines can be operated by anyone.

T – T.W. – G

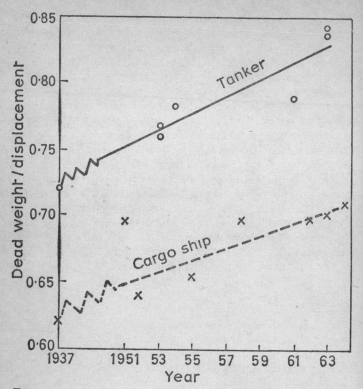

FIG. 2

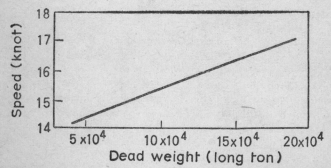

FIG. 3

Such computer applications are expected to be extended still more for 'on-line function' and 'on-demand computation', the former for the continuous supervision and control, in engine-room operation and collision warning, for example, and the latter made available as occasions demand, for example, to determine the ship's position or to reduce roll and pitch.

In the shipbuilding and ship-operating industries, all these points are currently under investigation, and the prospects for their realization are bright. Then, less than one third of the present number of crew will be quite sufficient for efficient and safe navigation.

All the predictions I have made are based on the extrapolation from the present state of things. Some may think them a little conservative.

Applications of Biology

MANUFACTURE BY TISSUE CULTURE

by Dr N. A. Mitchison

National Institute for Medical Research, Mill Hill

When Alexis Carrel discovered that cells could be grown outside the body in a glass flask, a new realm of biology seemed to open out. At first progress was slow, chiefly because of the difficulty of preserving the cultures from contamination with bacteria. An elaborate folklore of tissue culture grew up; assistants worked in masks and rubber gloves, in darkened rooms. These extravagant precautions quickly fell into disuse after the introduction of antibiotics. Salk signalled the inauguration of a new era ten years ago, when he announced that monkey kidney cells had been grown on a scale large enough to support commercial production of polio vaccine.

Cultured cells have come into use for vaccine production on a large scale. Wherever a parasite – bacteria, viruses, and recently even protozoa – will not grow in cell-free nutrients, tissue cultures are being tried.

Now that this has become a routine, what are the other products of cells which we can hope to obtain from cultures? Can we expect to make available all the complex materials which cells manufacture but which have so far proved inaccessible to chemical synthesis? These are not questions which need be discussed any longer in the abstract, for usable amounts of many useful things have already been made on a laboratory scale.

Hormones

Steroids and peptide hormones are made by cells cultured from the appropriate endocrine glands. The trouble here is that, as a rule, the cells lose their ability to produce hormones after a short time in culture. Eli Lilly and Co. have tried hard to obtain insulin from cultured pancreatic cells, and so avoid depending on the supply of glands from the slaughterhouses, but without success. Probably this is not just a matter of finding the correct nutrients. Cells seem to be very choosy about their neighbours, and prone to give up their more specialized activities – to 'de-differentiate' – when the structural organization of tissue is disrupted. Thyroid cells, for instance, remain healthy in tissue culture but stop producing thyroxine when the follicles fall apart. Perhaps plant cells which can synthesize steroids are the best for mass culture.

Antigens

Antigens have been extracted from the liver or spleen of mice and used to induce immunological tolerance, in order to be able subsequently to perform grafts of organs. This year for the first time antigens have been obtained successfully for this purpose from cultured cells. Manson in Philadelphia has not yet published the details of his work, but it seems that here the difficult step is to extract the antigens in soluble form from the cell membrane.

Antibodies

Cells from lymph glands, the spleen, and even the blood can synthesize appreciable amounts of antibody in culture. Unfortunately, here, as with the hormones, production soon falls off.

Enzymes

Cells grown in culture undoubtedly provide a rich source of enzymes. Many of the metabolic diseases are known to be caused by the deficiency of an enzyme. Defects or deficiencies in other types of protein may also manifest themselves as disease, defective haemoglobin causing sickle-cell anaemia, and lack of a serum protein causing a gamma-globulinaemia. Therapy by direct replacement has proved disappointing so far, chiefly because it has not been possible to insert the required protein into its correct place in the cell. Hope here lies in the possibility of replacing defective cells wholesale. This has been done in inbred mice, where congenital anaemia can be cured by transfusion of normal bone-marrow cells. In man a practical method of preventing rejection of the transfused cells has yet to be found.

When the problems have been solved, shall we depend entirely on tissue culture to provide these useful materials? Not entirely, for by 1984 our power to synthesize biological products without the intervention of cells will be much stronger. Much of this synthesis will proceed via routes unknown to cells – employing, for example, the highly ingenious tricks for joining peptide bonds which are at present revolutionizing the artificial synthesis of protein-like compounds.

Manufacture in tissue culture will enjoy the same sort of relationship to organic chemistry that bio-assay does at present to analytical chemistry. Products which today are synthesized and analysed by biological methods will tomorrow be dealt with by the chemist. This does not, of course, imply that the biological methods will fall into disuse; on the contrary, the most recently discovered and therefore most exciting products will always be manufactured and assayed biologically, while the chemist is hurrying to catch up.

Organic chemistry itself is subject to under-cutting by biochemistry. Purely chemical peptide synthesis, for example, has to begin with amino acids which are wholly 'left-handed', as in nature, if a biologically active product is to be obtained. Biochemical manufacture, on the other hand, exploits the ability of the cell's protein factories (the ribosomes) to reject 'right-handed' amino acids, and consequently needs less pure and far cheaper starting material.

Cells in culture will probably be used, therefore, to supply the instructions, coded in DNA or RNA, for other 'biological machines'. The machines themselves will perhaps be an undifferentiated general-purpose cell grown in culture; Pfizer and Co., I am told, already use viral nucleic acid according to this principle for vaccine production. Or the machines will perhaps be easily-grown bacterial cells, used as Abel in Cologne now uses *Bacillus subtilis* to grow vaccinia virus by nucleic-acid instruction. Or, again, the machinery may be completely cell-free – a vat of synthetic ribosomes.

CHANGING CELL HEREDITY

by Professor G. H. Beale, F.R.S.

Royal Society Research Professor, University of Edinburgh

When will it be possible to change the heredity of living cells in a controlled and predictable manner? We certainly cannot do so at present and one wonders whether the recent spectacular advances in our understanding of the chemical basis of heredity have made such a task realizable within the foreseeable future. First, let us consider the possibility of changing the most basic hereditary elements in cells, the genes, consisting – so we believe – of DNA.

Ever since H. J. Muller's discovery in 1927 that X-rays bring about gene mutation, a vast amount of work has been devoted to the artificial induction of mutations by various types of radiation and by chemical substances. However all such mutagens act in basically a random manner, merely increasing the statistical probability that a given gene will mutate, but never ensuring that a particular one will do so. And as is well known, the overwhelming majority of mutations are deleterious or even lethal.

Whether really specific chemical mutagens, producing a planned mutation in a chosen gene, will be produced seems doubtful, even though some (for example, analogues of adenine and thymine) have been thought to act directly on DNA. The genetic material consists, according to current theory, of endless combinations of only four basic chemical units, comprising a code. While it might conceivably be possible to change any one of these four units, leaving the others unaltered, obviously the agent used would not change one section of the genetic code, but almost the whole of it.

A more promising approach is one based on the phenomenon of 'transformation' in bacteria. Here DNA from one strain of bacteria is extracted, purified, and introduced into a second strain. The latter may then acquire some of the hereditary properties of the former. This technique has now been worked out in detail for a number of different bacterial species. However, no one has yet made a DNA preparation consisting of one gene only; the total DNA from a cell has to be used. In any case, transformation by means of extracted DNA has so far been achieved only with bacteria; various claims for the feasibility of a similar process in ducks and other higher animals have not been confirmed. In principle there seems no reason why selected foreign DNA should not be injected and incorporated into the chromosomes of higher organisms, but no one has succeeded in doing this yet, and there are formidable technical difficulties, especially in regard to gaining access to the sites of the genes in the nucleus in the middle of a cell.

Leaving aside this intractable problem of directly changing the genes, we may turn to other cell components which might more readily be handled, but whose roles are just as vital as those of the genes. In particular the substance RNA needs to be considered, and there the situation is beginning to look extremely interesting.

We believe nowadays that the DNA in the genes acts first to produce 'messenger RNA', which in turn controls the formation of specific proteins – notably enzymes – and ultimately of all the materials in the organism. The original 'messenger RNA' in bacteria was considered to be an extremely unstable substance, but later work with mammalian material showed that it might sometimes be more stable.

What are the possibilities of extracting specific messenger RNA from one cell and putting it into another? If this could be done it might be possible to transform a cell, at least temporarily, without introducing any DNA at all.

Recent work in Edinburgh and Indiana Universities has shown that it can be done. I. Gibson, T. M. Sonneborn, and I have been using as experimental material the single-celled animal *Paramecium*. It turns out that one particular hereditary property may be readily transferred from cell to cell by means of RNA- containing extracts.

The active principle, consisting of particles of RNA called 'metagons', certainly bears a gene 'message', conferring on the *Paramecium* the ability to maintain certain symbiotic bacterium-like particles in the cytoplasm and making the *Paramecium* a 'killer'. However metagons differ from the messenger RNA as originally defined in being extremely stable, both within the living cell and also in purified form outside. If such stable metagons should be found to control other hereditary characters in other species, and to be transferable from cell to cell and organism to organism, we shall have a valuable technique for changing the characters of cells in a controlled manner. Such changes would not be expected to be permanent: as the cells divide the introduced metagons would gradually become diluted and the genes of the recipient cells would alone control the type of cells formed in later generations.

However, there has recently been a most unexpected development in these investigations, indicating that under some conditions the metagons may replicate. When a *Paramecium* is eaten by a predator called *Didinium* (another ciliate protozoon), the *Didinium* ingests the *Paramecium*'s metagons, and these latter are not digested away but actually multiply at a rate sufficient to keep pace with the *Didinium*'s own reproduction (about four times a day). After a long period of culture of the *Didinium* the metagons can be re-infected into *Paramecium* and shown to possess their original properties of acting as gene-messengers. In a certain sense, in *Didinium* the metagons are more analogous to viruses than simply to messenger RNA, though in *Didinium* as in *Paramecium* the metagons exercise the characteristic messenger-like function of maintaining the killer particles. Thus the concepts of messenger RNA and virus seem to be becoming less separate than has been hitherto believed. In any case these experiments hint that it might even be possible to obtain a replicating form of messenger RNA.

It is to be expected that quite different methods of transforming cells from one type to another will be developed in the coming years. We must be prepared for surprises in this field of work – particularly in respect of structural differentiations between the various kinds of cells in multicellular organisms, for which the current 'molecular' theory of genetics offers very little enlightenment. Nevertheless there can be no doubt that by 1984 we shall have available vastly more potent techniques for changing cellular heredity than we know at present, and these will have great consequences for medicine and agriculture.

BIO-ENGINEERING: OPPORTUNITY WITHOUT LIMIT

by Professor R. M. Kenedi

Bio-engineering Unit, University of Strathclyde, Glasgow (Formerly Royal College of Science and Technology)

In recent years, the first signs of a counter-current of thinking have become manifest, opposing the ever-narrowing specialization of science. More and more scientists are realizing that the division of work into traditional or newly invented compartments is not only not 'natural' but is in fact inhibitive. The essential interconnexion of the life sciences and physical sciences, in particular, is giving rise to new interdisciplinary studies. One of these is bio-engineering.

One of the many aspects of bio-engineering is the study of the 'engineering' methods used by nature, with a view to applying the basic mechanisms in man-made engineering constructions. An example here is the 'feedback' control systems of living entities. One characteristic of a living system is that it grows and by some mechanisms in its growth develops capabilities which enable it to adapt to its environment – in short, it learns. These adaptive or learning processes are essentially manifestations of a variety of feed-back control mechanisms, and their study has led, for example, to aircraft control systems capable of self-correction. The numerous control systems of the body – for temperature, respiration, muscle, etc. – all present fields of fruitful study aimed at developing analogous engineering controls. The human body in itself is possibly the most complex multi-variable self-adaptive control system in existence, and a better understanding of its mode and pattern of operation should lead to better matching of machine and human operator.

The potential of this one aspect of bio-engineering alone is plainly enormous. By 1984 it will have afforded basically new concepts, which are therefore unpredictable in detail, leading to a wealth of control technologies inconceivable in present-day terms.

Bio-engineering also impinges on more traditional activities, such as the harnessing of biological systems, whether micro-organisms, plants, or animals, under controlled conditions to synthesize products which men need. One field in which techniques have to be worked out systematically, almost from scratch, is seafood farming. Experimental fish and oyster farms are now being initiated on an industrial scale and will no doubt expand in the next twenty years into a big industry utilizing the virtually inexhaustible food supply of the sea.

Environmental control, also part of bio-engineering, aims at providing optimum living conditions in closed and open systems. A typical closed system is that of a spacecraft where the human body, developed to exist and function in a gravitational field, has to be protected against a variety of physiological effects arising out of weightlessness. Intensive human-engineering research is now in progress, and one confidently expects by 1984 the translation of today's pioneer adventure into a matter of everyday routine. Environmental control of various facets of open systems – for example the occupational health requirements of large communities – should reach a stage by 1984 where homes, offices, cities will be designed to serve the scientifically assessed physical and psychological requirements of the individual, perhaps using, where necessary, artificially created atmospheres within huge enclosures.

The upsurge of interest has nowhere been more evident than in a remaining major aspect of bio-engineering – its applications in the field of medicine. The range and scope of the achievements of medical engineering in the past decade alone are staggering: ultrasonic echo-sounding techniques for diagnoses; electronic pacemakers and defibrillators which correct uncoordinated heart motion; 'radio pills' which transmit information from within the body; and many others. Evaluation of the mechanical and structural characteristics of human tissue, their load-carrying capacities and their functional role in the body, assist the development of treatment, particularly in reparative surgery. There is also a whole new technology developing, concerned with artificial replacements for damaged body components. A variety of prosthetic devices ranging from plastic heart valves to artificial limbs are being developed, and there is real promise of certain artificial limbs being operated by electric impulses generated in appropriately connected muscles by the individual thinking of the movements he desires to make. As miniaturization proceeds, the possibility of artificial kidney and heart-lung machines becoming available in implantable form is no longer unbelievable. By 1984, artificial replacements for tissues and organs may well have become commonplace.

This brief summary of the prospects for bio-engineering is based on progress in the past decade, which we now see accelerating at a phenomenal rate. Prediction of the shape of things to come twenty years hence in any definite form is impossible, not because of lack of visible trends, but, on the contrary, because the potential is so enormous.

ISOLATING CELL MACHINERY

by Professor Robert Brown, F.R.S.

Department of Botany, University of Edinburgh

The green plant is the most extensive synthetic machine in nature. Normally it has available to it from the environment a limited number of inorganic compounds, water, carbon dioxide and oxygen. From these it synthesizes all the major compounds required by other organisms, including man. Moreover it has the further characteristic that the energy for the synthesis of all these compounds is either immediately or ultimately derived from sunlight. Clearly, if the synthetic processes that are sustained by the green plant could be reproduced in an artificial system, they would vastly increase the range of compounds that can now be produced on an industrial scale, and at the same time might have an effect on the sources of energy available to industry.

These possibilities have provided some of the motives for the study of metabolic processes in plants, but there have been others. An intimate knowledge of the synthetic processes themselves raises the less spectacular but perhaps more immediately realizable possibility of stimulating the production of particular compounds in the growing plant itself.

The study of metabolic processes in general and of synthetic processes in particular has been greatly facilitated by the development of techniques for the isolation of the 'organelles' of cells. The largest of these organelles is the nucleus but in addition there are, amongst others, chloroplasts, mitochondria and ribosomes, with each of which different metabolic processes are associated. They can be isolated by breaking all the cells, releasing the organelles into an appropriate solution and then centrifuging them.

At present two general fields of work seem to hold the richest promise of practical application in the future. These are the syntheses (1) of different carbohydrates, and (2) of nitrogenous compounds, particularly proteins.

The photosynthesis of carbohydrates, wherein light energy absorbed by chlorophyll evokes the formation of sugars from carbon dioxide and water, has been intensively studied in recent years, particularly in the U.S.A. In terms of 1984 one possibility may be noted. Frequently, the productivity of the green plant is limited by the concentration of carbon dioxide in the air (about 0·04 per cent). This concentration can be raised artificially in a confined atmosphere such as that of a greenhouse, with an increase in productivity. There seems some possibility that a cheap enough supply of carbon dioxide may become available from the byproducts of oil refineries.

It has now been established that the whole photosynthetic process is completed in the chloroplast. This organelle is an oval body about 5–6 microns in length (a micron being a thousandth of a millimetre). Two zones have been distinguished in the chloroplast, the grana, which has an intricate structural pattern, and the stroma, which is apparently a clear amorphous matrix. The chlorophyll is carried in the grana, where the light energy it absorbs cleaves water molecules (releasing oxygen) and makes available both hydrogen and the energy-carrying molecule ATP. Carbon dioxide is probably 'fixed' in the stroma, and is converted to a sugar by 'dark reactions' that can occur in the absence of light but depend on the products of the 'light reactions'.

All the enzymes involved in the 'dark reactions' and the course of the reactions, are now probably known. This being the case it is conceivable that an artificial system could be set up which would yield sugar when it is exposed to carbon dioxide. The system would have (1) to incorporate a source of reducing power, (2) to carry ATP together with the whole series of enzymes involved in the natural process, (3) to secure appropriate relative rates for the different reactions, and (4) ensure a continuous removal of the products. None of these requirements is theoretically impossible and, by 1984, there will probably be no practical difficulty in obtaining the appropriate enzymes in pure form.

The industrial production of sugar would be a development of major significance. It would stimulate other developments, one of which may be mentioned here. The industrial cotton fibre is basically the wall of a plant cell, and its significant component is cellulose in which successive glucose units are linked together in a chain. It is one of the oddities of textile research that it has never extended to the investigation of the mechanism of cellulose synthesis, but this has recently been analysed in non-industrial laboratories and knowledge about it is accumulating rapidly. By 1984 the whole system will certainly be well-established and if a large supply of glucose is then available it may be possible to devise a system for the artificial synthesis of cellulose. With this development the possibility arises that cotton may regain some of the ground it has lost to 'synthetic' fibres.

Less is known about the course of the light reactions in photosynthesis, but the recent discovery that ATP is produced is extremely significant. ATP (adenosine triphosphate) is the form in which energy is transferred in cells. It has a series of three phosphate groups, the last of which is attached by a chemical bond of high energy.

The formation of ATP by photosynthesis can be induced in the laboratory without the fixation of carbon dioxide. This achievement suggests the possibility of a corresponding development on an industrial scale. It would provide a source of heat from the most readily available form of energy, namely sunlight – a form of energy, be it said, which has never been extensively exploited. The probability of this end being attained by 1984 is, however, slight. The mechanisms involved in the light reactions in the elaborate structure of the grana are still a matter of speculation.

The natural synthesis of proteins and other nitrogenous compounds in plants depends on the availability of combined nitrogen. The level of combined nitrogen in the soil is usually limiting for plant growth, which is why nitrogenous artificial fertilizers are used. These nitrogenous fertilizers are produced industrially by reducing nitrogen from air to ammonia, but the energy required is very large and the fertilizers are consequently expensive. This fact, amongst others, has recently stimulated interest in the nitrogen fixation by micro-organisms in the soil and in the nodules of leguminous plants. The natural process occurs at normal temperatures and pressures and the study of this may therefore lead to the discovery of cheaper industrial methods, or, alternatively, enable us to stimulate the natural process and so make artificial fertilizer less necessary. While the latter may well be attained by 1984, it is doubtful if knowledge of the natural process could be incorporated into a new industrial method by then. Fixation has already been recorded in a cell-free extract, but the analysis is far from complete.

Perhaps the two most significant nitrogenous compounds synthesized in plant – and other cells – are proteins and nucleic acids. Of the two, the proteins are certainly the more abundant; they are the basis of metabolic activity, and they constitute one of the major components in the diets of animals and man. Anything which holds even the vaguest promise of providing the basis for artificial synthesis of proteins is particularly tantalizing. But the difficulties are enormous. There are many kinds of proteins and although they are built from a common set of amino acids, there are at least twenty-four of these involved.

The formation of the constituent amino acids involves the participation of another cell organelle, the mitochondrion, which is frequently a spherical body about 1–2 microns in diameter. Here the last vital stages of respiration are completed, and during this process certain acids are formed which may combine with ammonia to give amino acids. It is conceivable that this system could be adapted to a large-scale production of amino acids.

The synthesis of the proteins themselves almost certainly occurs on the surfaces of the smallest organelles in the cell or on the surfaces of derivatives of these. The organelles are the ribosomes which are more or less spherical bodies of the order of one fiftieth of a micron in diameter, and chemically their main component is ribose-nucleic acid (RNA). The ribosomes marshal the various amino acids in the required sequence and form the peptide bonds which link the amino acids together. The first activity depends on the presence of 'messenger RNA' derived from the cell nucleus and it gives the sequence appropriate to a particular protein. The formation of the peptide bonds depends on different catalytic systems and on the presence of a variety of substances, particularly of ATP.

Ribosomes are readily isolated from cells and it is possible that, so isolated, they could form the basis for a large-scale production of protein. That could be done, however, only if the other components required in the synthesis were also supplied. This implies an independent large-scale isolation of the different messengers and their addition to the system – a formidable undertaking which may not be achieved by 1984.

At the same time, it is significant that, three years ago, in a system containing one amino acid (phenylalanine), ribosomes, and a polyuricylic acid (acting as an artificial messenger RNA) the synthesis of a protein-like substance, polyphenylalanine, was demonstrated. Subsequently more complex artificial messengers have been used to evoke the formation of other materials. The products are, so far, very different from natural protein, but large-scale synthesis of protein is now at least a plausible possibility.

Notes on the Contributors

NIGEL CALDER has been editor of *New Scientist* since 1962. Educated at Cambridge he worked for two years as a physicist for Mullard Research Laboratories before joining the staff of *New Scientist* at its inception in 1956.

ALEXANDER ROBERTUS TODD (Working with what we know) is Master of Christ's College and Professor of Organic Chemistry in the University of Cambridge. He was awarded the Nobel Prize for Chemistry in 1957 and created a life peer in 1962. He is Chancellor of the University of Strathclyde.

ISIDOR ISAAC RABI (The scientist in public affairs) has been Associate Director of the Radiation Laboratory of the Massachusetts Institute of Technology, and Chairman of the general advisory committee to the Atomic Energy Commission. He has been Higgins Professor of Physics at Columbia University since 1950, and is a member of the President's Science Advisory Committee. He was awarded the Nobel Prize for Physics in 1944.

ABDUS SALAM (How can we be optimists?) is engaged in research on the theory of elementary particles at Imperial College, London, where he is Professor of Theoretical Physics. He is also Chief Scientific Adviser to the President of Pakistan and a member of the Pakistan Atomic Energy Commission.

JOHN DOUGLAS COCKCROFT (Towards a better understanding of natural forces) is Master of Churchill College, Cambridge, and a member of the board of the National Institute for Research in Nuclear Science. He has been Director of the Atomic Energy Research Establishment and a Member for Research of the United Kingdom Atomic Energy Authority. He was knighted in 1948, and shared the Nobel Prize for Physics in 1951.

NORBERT WIENER (Dynamical systems in physics and biology) gained his Ph.D. at Harvard at the age of eighteen, and continued his work in Germany and England. He was Professor Emeritus at the Massachusetts Institute of Technology and had been attached to the faculty of mathematics from 1919 until his death in 1964. He is the author of *Cybernetics*.

JOSHUA LEDERBERG (A crisis in evolution) is Professor of Genetics and Director of the J. P. Kennedy Jr. Laboratories for Molecular Medicine at Stanford University, California. He was awarded the Nobel Prize for Medicine and Physiology in 1958.

FRED HOYLE (A new physics out of astronomy?) is forty-eight. He was educated at Emmanuel College, Cambridge. He has been Plumian Professor of Astronomy and Experimental Philosophy at Cambridge since 1958, and is a Fellow of St John's College. His books include *The Nature of the Universe, Frontiers of Astronomy*, and *A Decade of Decision*.

HARRIE STEWART WILSON MASSEY (Scientific purposes in space) is an Australian who came to Britain over thirty years ago. He is chairman of the British National Committee for Space Research, President of the European Space Research Organization, and Quain Professor of Physics at University College, London. He was knighted in 1960.

GERALD CONNOP GROSS (Telecommunications in space exploration) was born in New York, and educated in France and Haverford College, Pennsylvania. He is the Secretary-General of the International Telecommunications Union in Geneva. He holds the Gold Medal of Achievement of the Veteran Wireless Operators Association for his service to world communications.

WERNHER MAGNUS MAXIMILIAN VON BRAUN (Exploration to the farthest planets) was born in 1912 in Germany. He went to the U.S.A. in 1945. He is now the Director of the George C. Marshall Space Flight Center of the National Aeronautics and Space Administration. He led the development of the Jupiter C rocket that launched America's first satellite.

PIERRE LAFFITTE (Mineral ores: a challenge to Europe) is thirty-nine. He was educated at the École Polytechnique and at the École Nationale Supérieure des Mines, of which he is deputy head. Until recently he was Associate Director-General of the Bureau de Recherches Géologiques et Minières. He has published widely on mining, geology, and mineralogy.

MICHEL BATISSE (Learning the value of water) is forty-one. He was educated at the École Centrale de Paris. He is the Chief of the Natural Resources Research Division of UNESCO. Previously he has worked in the Cairo Regional Science Office and in the Arid Zone Research Programme of the organization.

FRANÇOIS BOURLIÈRE (A new balance between man and nature) is fifty. He is Professor of Gerontology of the Faculty of Medicine at

Paris University, where he received the degrees of M.D. and L.Sc. He is President of the International Union for the Conservation of Nature and Natural Resources. He has published a number of books including *The Natural History of Mammals*.

EDWARD MAX NICHOLSON (Orchestrating the use of land) is fifty-nine. He was educated at Hertford College, Oxford. He has been Director-General of the Nature Conservancy, London, since 1952. As well as being convener of the conservation section of the International Biological Programme, he is a member of the Advisory Council on Scientific Policy. He has written several books including *Britain's Nature Reserves*.

BINAY RANJAN SEN (The race will not yet be won) has been Indian Ambassador to several countries, including the United States. He is now Director-General of the Food and Agriculture Organization, Rome. He initiated the Freedom from Hunger Campaign. He was educated at Calcutta and Oxford Universities.

WILLIAM KERSHAW SLATER (Farming as a science-based industry) was educated at Manchester University. He was Secretary of the Agricultural Research Council from 1949 to 1960, and has been Regent's Lecturer at the Davis campus of the University of California. He is chairman of the Projects Committee of the Freedom from Hunger Campaign. He was knighted in 1951.

JOHN YUDKIN (Beware the malnutrition of affluence) studied medicine at Cambridge and the London Hospital, and became Director of Medical Studies at Christ's College from 1940 to 1943. He is now Professor of Nutrition and Dietetics at Queen Elizabeth College, London, where he previously held the chair of Physiology. He is the author of *This Slimming Business*.

HAROLD HARTLEY (World energy prospects) is a physical chemist and an expert in fuel and power. He has been President of the World Power Conference, chairman of the energy commission of OEEC, chairman of the Fuel Research Board, and adviser to the Ministry of Fuel and Power. He was knighted in 1928.

JULES GUÉRON (The uses of energy) is Director-General of the research and training division of the European Atomic Energy Commission, Brussels. He has been concerned with atomic energy since 1941 and is at present secretary of the commission of Atomic Weights of the International Union of Pure and Applied Chemistry.

IAN FELLS (New sources of electricity) was educated at Trinity College, Cambridge. He has been lecturer on fuel technology and chemical engineering in the University of Sheffield, and is now reader in fuel science in the University of Newcastle-upon-Tyne. He is responsible for all teaching and research in this subject there.

ROBERT ALLAN SMITH (Designing the materials we need) was educated at Edinburgh, and Cambridge, England. Until 1961 he was head of the physics department of the Royal Radar Establishment, Malvern. He is now Professor of Physics and Director of the Center for Materials Science at the Massachusetts Institute of Technology. He was awarded the C.B.E. in 1960. He has written many books, including *Semiconductors* and *Wave Mechanics of Crystalline Solids*.

WALTER ERIC DUCKWORTH (Stronger steel for wider purposes) is thirty-eight, and was educated at Cambridge. He was operations research manager of the Glacier Metal Company for five years and is now head of the metallurgy division of the British Iron and Steel Research Association. He is the author of *A Guide to Operational Research*.

JAMES DENNING PEARSON (Working with new materials) is fifty-five. He has been with Rolls-Royce since 1932. He was made Managing Director of the Aero-Engine Division in 1954, and is now Chief Executive and Deputy Chairman of the company. He was knighted in 1963, and is President of the Society of British Aerospace Companies.

PIERRE ÉTIENNE BÉZIER (High-speed automatic workshops) is fifty-four, and was educated at the École des Arts et Métiers, Paris, and the École Supérieure d'Électricité. He has been with Régie Renault, Billancourt, since 1933, and is now director of the company. He is concerned in particular with the production side.

ALISTER CLAVERING HARDY (New and richer marine harvests forecast) is an Emeritus Professor of the University of Oxford, where he held the Linacre Chair of Zoology from 1946 to 1961. He has also been Chief Zoologist to the Discovery Expedition and Professor of Zoology and Oceanography at University College, Hull. He is a knight, and author of *The Open Sea*, and other works.

EDWIN ALBERT LINK (Working deep in the sea) is the inventor of the Link Aviation Trainer. He has been President of General Precision Systems, and before that Chairman of the Executive Committee of the Link Division of General Precision Inc. He holds several medals and is co-author of *Simplified Celestial Navigation*.

ROGER REVELLE (A long view from the beach) was Professor of Oceanography at the Scripp's Institution, University of California from 1948 to 1950 when he became its Director. He has been Dean of

Research of the University, and science adviser to the U.S. Secretary of the Interior. He has served on the U.S. National Commission for UNESCO, and has led several oceanographic expeditions.

OLIVER GRAHAM SUTTON (Steady progress in techniques of forecasting) is Director-General of the Meteorological Office. He has been Professor of Mathematical Physics and Dean of the Royal Military College of Science. He is Chairman of the National Committee for Geodesy and Geophysics. He was knighted in 1955.

FRED SINGER (The World Weather Satellite System) is thirty-nine. He was Director of the National Weather Satellite Center of the U.S. Weather Bureau, and also has been Professor in the Physics Department of the University of Maryland. He is now Dean of the School of Environmental and Plantary Sciences in the University of Miami, Florida. He has written *Progress in Astronautical Sciences*.

DAVID ARTHUR DAVIES (Meteorology and human activity) was born in 1913. He is now Secretary-General of the World Meteorological Organization, and is responsible for its technical and administrative work.

HENDRIK WILLEM SLOTBOOM (Plenitude from petroleum) is fifty-eight. He is Professor of Chemical Technology at the Technological University, Eindhoven, and scientific adviser to Shell Internationale Research Maatschappij NV. He has been working for the Royal Dutch Shell organization for many years, and was Director of Research of their Amsterdam laboratories for eight years.

KOICHI YAMADA (Chemistry and living organisms) was born in 1912, and educated at the University of Tokyo where he is a Professor in the Department of Agricultural Chemistry.

GIULIO NATTA (The ascendancy of giant molecules) was born in 1903. He has been Director of the Institute of Industrial Chemistry at the Milan Polytechnic since 1938. A chemical engineer by training, he shared the Nobel Prize for Chemistry in 1963. He is an honorary life member of the New York Academy of Sciences.

LIONEL DE BOURNONVILLE (The customer's ideal computer) is forty-four. He is now technical adviser to Compagnie des Machines Bull, France, having previously worked in their export department. He is an engineer by training.

ARTHUR LEE SAMUEL (The banishment of paper-work) is sixty-two. He is consultant to the Director of Research of I.B.M., New York, and also Visiting Professor of Electrical Engineering at the

Massachusetts Institute of Technology. He was formerly with the Bell Telephone Laboratories, and was Professor of Electrical Engineering at the University of Illinois.

MAURICE VINCENT WILKES (A world dominated by computers?) was a pioneer of computers in Britain. He is now Director of the University Mathematical Laboratory at Cambridge. From 1957 to 1960 he was the first President of the British Computer Society.

JOHN ROBINSON PIERCE (Private television instead of travel) is fifty-three. He is Executive Director of Research, Communications Systems and Communications Principles Divisions at the Bell Telephone Laboratories, and also Visiting Distinguished Professor of Engineering Physics at the University of Nevada. He gained the National Medal of Science in 1964.

JOHN DICKENS CLARE (Decentralization by telecommunications) was educated at the University of Birmingham. He has been director of guided weapons research and development, Ministry of Aviation, and is now Managing Director and Director of Research of the Standard Telecommunication Laboratories, Harlow.

GERALD REID BARRY (Mass communications in 1984) was editor of the *Saturday Review* from 1924 to 1930 and of the *News Chronicle* from 1936 to 1947. From 1948 to 1951 he was Director-General of the Festival of Britain. He is now an executive of Granada TV. He was knighted in 1951.

MICHAEL JAMES LIGHTHILL (Market needs and technical possibilities) is Royal Society Professor at Imperial College, University of London. Until October 1964 he was Director of the Royal Aircraft Establishment at Farnborough. He is the author of *Introduction to Fourier Analysis and Generalized Functions*.

PIERRE SATRE (Travelling by air in 1984) was educated at the École Polytechnique and the École Nationale Supérieure de l'Aéronautique. He is now Technical Manager of Sud-Aviation, and is well-known for his work on the Caravelle airliner.

RONALD MACALISTER MACDONNELL (Towards complete safety in the air) is fifty-five, and was educated at the University of Manitoba and at Oxford. He has been Deputy Secretary of State for External Affairs in Canada, and is now Secretary-General of the International Civil Aviation Organization, Montreal, Canada.

CHRISTOPHER SYDNEY COCKERELL (The prospects for hover transport) was educated at Peterhouse College, Cambridge. He is the inventor of the Hovercraft. He was formerly in charge of the airborne development section of the Marconi Company and is now Chairman of the Ripplecraft Company and a director and technical consultant of Hovercraft Development.

CAMILLE MARTIN (The railways of tomorrow) is fifty-eight. He is traction and rolling stock manager of the Société National des Chemins de Fer (SNCF) of France, and president of the board of directors for traction and rolling stock, and of the fifth Commission of the Union Internationale des Chemins de Fer.

WILLIAM HENRY GLANVILLE (Roads and traffic in 1984) is Director of Road Research in the Department of Scientific and Industrial Research, and chairman of several national and international committees on road problems. In 1957 he was Chairman of the International Road Safety Research Conference. He was president of the Institution of Civil Engineers for a year, and was knighted in 1960.

YOSHIHIRO WATANABE (How big will ships become ?) was educated at the University of Tokyo. He is an Emeritus Professor of Kyushu University, and is technical adviser to the Sasebo Heavy Industrial Company, the Mitsubishi Shipbuilding Company, and the Hitachi Shipbuilding and Engineering Company. He has been President of the Society of Naval Architects of Japan.

NICHOLAS AVRION MITCHISON (Manufacture by tissue culture) is head of the Experimental Biology Division of the National Institute for Medical Research. Previously he lectured in zoology at the University of Edinburgh and is a medallist of the Zoological Society.

GEOFFREY HERBERT BEALE (Changing cell heredity) is Royal Society Research Professor at Edinburgh University. After the war he did research at the Carnegie Institute in New York and was Rockefeller Fellow at Indiana University. He was elected Fellow of the Royal Society in 1959.

ROBERT M. KENEDI (Bio-engineering: opportunity without limit) is Professor of Bio-engineering at Strathclyde University. He has worked as consultant, researcher and university lecturer in the fields of civil, mechanical, and structural engineering.

ROBERT BROWN (Isolating cell machinery) is Professor of Botany at Edinburgh University. He has been Professor of Botany at Cornell University and Director of the Agricultural Research Council Unit of Plant Cell Physiology. He was elected Fellow of the Royal Society in 1960.

Some other Penguin and Pelican books are
described on the following pages

SPACE IN THE SIXTIES
Patrick Moore

Patrick Moore, an astronomer, was among the first
prophets of space travel thirty years ago. In this
sober and up-to-the-minute report he sets down
the present 'state of work' outside the atmosphere.
It is an account to stagger the imagination.
Unimagined speeds; seemingly immeasurable
distances; intolerable extremes of temperature;
calculations of infinite precision; a limbo of
weightlessness and airlessness where nothing
falls, nothing breathes – all these had to be
mastered before a man could have the *mappa
mundi* view of Earth described by Gagarin.

We are witnessing the birth of a wholly new
technique of human movement and the author of
this book allows us a more intimate account of
the training and the feats of the astronauts than is
ever possible in a newspaper.

And after the unmanned probes and the first
orbital flights ? What more will the sixties – this
decisive decade – show us ? A road to the stars ?
Life – or the possibility of life – in other worlds ?
New wealth, new power ? In answering our
queries, Patrick Moore parades an array of
scientific facts that are stranger than science
fiction.

The following are the contents of the two volumes:

PENGUIN SCIENCE SURVEY 1965

The following are the contents of the two volumes:

A

High Field Superconductivity: K. Mendelssohn.
Surface Structures of Crystals and Low-energy Electron Diffraction: J. J. Lander.
Flash Photolysis and Shock Waves: Peter Borrell.
Physics of the Brain: W. Grey Walter. *Automated Spacecraft of the United States*: Edgar M. Cortright.
Operational Research: Patrick Rivett.
Diamonds in Industry: S. Tolansky.
Reactive Dyes: R. H. Peters.
Rubber: Leonard Mullins.
The Supersonic Airliner: John Taylor.
High Speed Propulsion of the Future: J. G. Keenan.
The Communication of Information: Colin Cherry.
Science on Radio: John Newell.

B

Intelligence: Convergent and Divergent: Liam Hudson.
Stratagems for Skill: Ian M. L. Hunter.
On Drawing a Diamond: M. L. J. Abercrombie.
Machine Intelligence: Donald Michie.
The Investigation of Mental Images: Peter McKellar.
Sleeping and Dreaming: Ian Oswald.
Physique and Athletic Performance: J. M. Tanner.
Some Problems of Homosexuality: E. Maurice Backett.
Tranquillizers and Mental Illness: J. R. Roy.
The Yeasts of Wine: James Barnett.
Penicillinase: M. R. Pollock.
Lymphocytes, Lymphoid Tissue, And Immunity: J. L. Gowans.
Leukaemia: W. M. Court Brown.

THE RISE OF THE MERITOCRACY
Michael Young

Dr Michael Young has christened the oligarchy of the future 'Meritocracy' – and the word is now part of the language. For it would appear that the formula I.Q.+effort=MERIT may well constitute the basic belief of the ruling class of the next century. Projecting himself into the year 2034, the author of this telling satire shows how present decisions and practices may re-mould our society.

Already today it is no longer enough to be somebody's nephew to obtain a responsible post in the civil service, in teaching, in science, or in commerce. Experts in education and selection apply scientific principles to sift out the leaders of tomorrow. You need intelligence rating, qualification, experience, application, and a certain calibre to achieve status – in a word, you must show 'merit'. Is this an undivided blessing?

'Its wit, its style, and its continuous fountain-gush of new ideas make it compulsively enjoyable reading from cover to cover' – *Time and Tide*

'Brilliant essay' – *Guardian*

THE INTELLIGENT WOMAN'S GUIDE TO ATOMIC RADIATION
Margot Bennett

In the most real sense women are more creative and less destructive than men. This Penguin Special, which is so intimately concerned with life and inheritance, has therefore deliberately been called *The Intelligent Woman's Guide to Atomic Radiation*. It is, if you wish, a translation into plain English of ugly things that are more normally referred to in the foreign language of Science.

Here you will find a clear but accurate account of the atom and its nucleus, of natural radio-activity, ionizing radiations, fission and fusion. You can read about the bomb, about fall-out, armaments, Civil Defence, protective measures, pollution, and the uses and dangers of radiation . . . and understand what you are reading.

In short, Margot Bennett has succeeded in providing a first reader in the most uncomfortable subject in the world.

THE FUTURE OF THE WELFARE STATE
D. C. Marsh

Did Britain construct a Welfare State so that we could sit back and admire it? And, now that the building has been occupied for some years, is it so admirable?

This Penguin Special puts the magnifying glass on an achievement about which we are in danger of becoming too complacent. Arguing that a Welfare State is not a Welfare State unless it serves, first and foremost, the needs of the citizen, the author, who is the Professor of Social Science at Nottingham University, suggests that a twentieth-century concept is being negatived by the nineteenth-century structure of our central and local administration. Already administrative convenience (one of the occupational ailments of bureaucracy) is beginning to alter the whole spirit of the enterprise. The ideals which originally inspired it are crystallizing, before our eyes, into a vast, self-perpetuating vested interest, armed with printed forms and procedures.

A minority may dislike the Welfare State on principle. David Marsh warns us, however, that it is far more gravely threatened by the inertia of the machine itself, which is due for overhaul, and, probably, re-modelling.

For a complete list of books available please write to Penguin Books, whose address can be found on the back of the title page